GOOD LOOKS
FOR LIFE

GOOD LOOKS FOR LIFE

LIZ E LONDON
and
ANNE H ADAMS

HAMLYN

To our parents, our husbands, our children.
To Alexandra-Mia.
To life.

First published in 1990 by
the Hamlyn Publishing Group Limited,
a division of the Octopus Publishing Group,
Michelin House, 81 Fulham Road,
London SW3 6RB

Editor **Anna Mumford**
Art Editor **Lisa Tai**
Production Controller **Amanda Sneddon**
Picture Research **Emily Hedges**

ISBN 0 600 57088 6

Typeset by Flair plan
Produced by Mandarin Offset – printed in Hong Kong.

CONTENTS

Introduction

Welcome to *Good Looks for Life!*

After we published our first book, we were over-whelmed with calls from women approaching 40 or more who were concerned about their changing fashion and beauty needs. They wanted to update their appearance and rethink their image in keeping with the times. They wanted looks that would express their individuality and suit their lifestyles. Above all, they wanted beautiful, wearable clothes that would move in and out of the wardrobe and make them look great and feel great. *Good Looks for Life* is written for these women, and for the woman of today who is interested in looking her best.

Now is the time to take charge of looking and feeling your best for the rest of your life. Caring for skin and hair, exercising your body and developing new interests are just as important as clothes and cosmetics. Go back to college; acquire a new skill. A woman who has enthusiasm and individuality is full of vitality and ageless.

So turn your back on those stiff, structured outfits, explore new make-up ideas, be bold with accessories, wear new colours, dare to be different and, above all, enjoy life!

Liz E. London.   *Anne Adams*

S*kin*

C A R E · B A T H · F R A G R A N C E S

We all strive for fresh, youthful-looking skin and want to know how to keep it looking its best. From our teens onwards, we need to practise a daily skincare routine to keep our skin healthy, vibrant and attractive. With developments in recent years, every-one can have younger looking skin and keep it looking better longer. We can improve the overall elasticity and resilience of the skin; we can make skin smoother by improving surface texture; we can provide protection against sun and environmental dam-age; and we can eliminate signs of dryness and flakiness. There are three golden rules:

SKIN CHANGES CONSTANTLY

– WITH YOUR EMOTIONS, YOUR AGE,

YOUR ENVIRONMENT AND THE EVENTS OF

THE MOMENT. IT NEEDS A LIFETIME OF

CONSTANT CARE.

Dr Erno Laszlo

Protect your skin with a sunscreen

Sunscreens allow you to tan without burning. The sun protection factors range from 2 up to about 39. Start with the highest protection and then work down, in-creasing protection when the sun is at its hottest. Once you get the tan you want, you can maintain it with a lower number sunscreen.

Nourish your skin with water

Drink at least six glasses of water a day. A high water content is the best way to make your skin look younger. Each day you lose about 3½ pints of water through the skin. Daily moisture loss accentuates every little wrinkle.

Know your skin type and how to care for it

Everyone's skin is slightly different. Work out your skin type and then follow the appropriate routine.

Dry skin

Cleanse with a very mild super-fatted cream soap or a rich cleansing lotion. (If your skin feels dry or looks red or flaky after cleansing, you are using the wrong soap or cleanser.) Never put make-up directly on your face; always use a moisturizer first. Avoid strong astringents and drying face masks. At night, protect the delicate skin under your eyes – with the tip of a finger dot on eye cream from outer eye corner to inner, then smooth into the skin gently.

Tip Try to avoid too much heat or too much cold.

Normal skin

Cleanse with a mild cleanser and rinse thoroughly with at least three to four rinses of warm (not hot) water to remove any traces of cleanser. Apply a light layer of moisturizer to the areas of your skin that feel dry or taut. Gently dot eye cream around the delicate area of your eyes, and then smooth on without dragging the skin.

Tip Cold weather is drying to the skin. Apply a richer moisturizer when going out in the cold, being sure to include the throat and eye area.

Oily skin

Use a rough face cloth or abrasive cleansing sponge to whisk off dull film and build-up of dead skin cells. Apply a water-based moisturizer to any dry areas and an eye cream under the eyes. With a cotton ball, apply toner to the oily parts of your face.

Tip Heat and humidity make the skin more oily. Cleanse your face more often during warm weather.

1 Apply cleansing cream to face.

2 Use eye make-up remover pads to clean the eye area.

3 With a cotton bud, gently remove any remaining eye make-up.

4 Twice a month, use a deep-cleansing exfoliating mask to remove impurities from the skin. A peel-off mask also makes your skin feel softer and more taut.

5 Remove mask (if you have applied one) and close the pores with toner using a pad of cotton wool. Toning is an important step in the daily cleansing routine.

6 Apply three dots of moisturizer to cheeks and forehead, then blend in circular strokes.

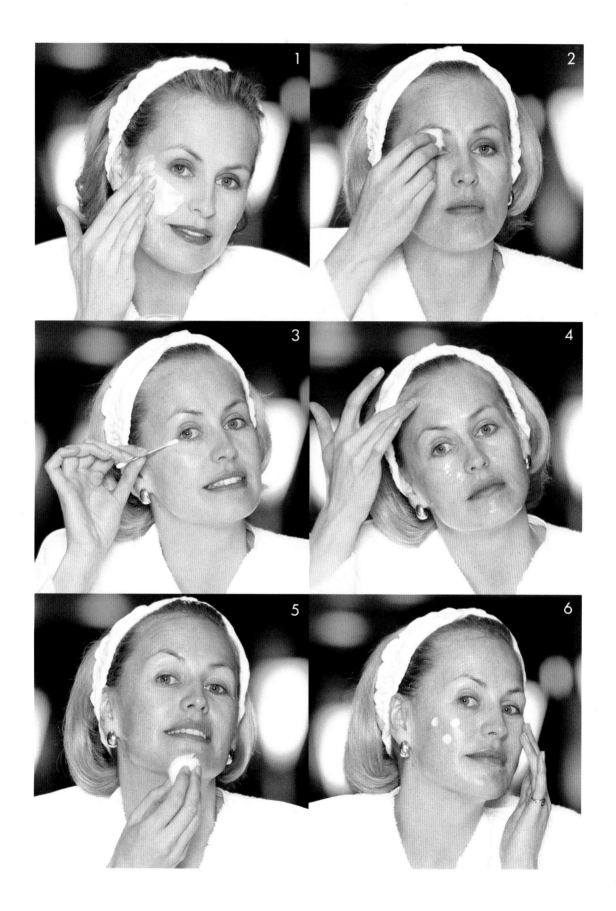

SKIN CARE

There are four essential elements to skin care: cleansing, toning, exfoliating and moisturizing.

Cleansing

Cleansing plays *the* most important role in skin care. Skin which is not properly cleansed cannot breathe. Proper cleansing removes make-up, dirt, cellular debris and helps prevent a build-up of dead skin cells.

Cleansing creams and lotions are not as drying as soap. Creams are usually richer than lotions which have a higher percentage of water. Eye and throat creams contain ingredients to tighten the eye and throat areas while lubricating them. All mature skins need the lubricating protection of eye creams.

Toning

After cleansing the face, apply a toner or mild astringent. A toner continues the cleansing process by removing all traces of soap or cleanser. It closes the pores and leaves the skin totally clean and refreshed.

Exfoliating

This process is a deep cleansing treatment that removes dead cells and impurities from the surface of the skin. Exfoliators include: lotions, gentle scrubs, a rough facecloth, a coarse sponge, a complexion brush or, for the body, a bigger, stiffer brush.

Exfoliation is especially helpful for mature skin because older skin does not shed cells as fast as it once did. Here is what it can do for you:
- stimulate circulation and help the skin breathe;
- clear the skin of the dirt, pollutants, cellular debris and excess oils that make the skin look coarse and older;
- make the skin appear smoother and plumper.
- gives the skin colour and tone.

Caution If your skin is very delicate or very sensitive, avoid harsh exfoliators and skin scrubbing. Always apply a moisturizer after you exfoliate. The best way to use a moisturizer is to smooth it over damp skin.

Moisturizing

Moisturizer is a must! It slows down moisture loss and protects the skin from the harmful effects of the environment which dry out the skin. Moisturizers are now available with built-in sun screens to protect you against the harmful rays of the sun. Some are specially formulated for dry skin. These are thicker and offer better protection against moisture loss. The effect should not be greasy; if yours is, try a lighter one. Apply moisturizer to slightly damp skin after it has been cleansed — if you have the time, allow it to soak into the skin for about 20 minutes before applying foundation. For a healthy outdoor glow, try a tinted moisturizer.

SPECIAL SKIN TREATMENTS

Whatever your skin type, an occasional mask treatment will make your face feel clean and look radiant.

Face or beauty mask

A good face mask improves the circulation, draws out impurities, tightens pores and seals in moisturizer. It

CALENDAR OF HEALTH AND BEAUTY

DAILY
Drink water
Exercise
Moisturize face
Floss teeth
Cleanse face applying cream to
  face and throat nightly

WEEKLY
Manicure
Shampoo
Pluck eyebrows
Exercise class
Treat rough heels and elbows
Shave legs, underarms
Do something fun!

MONTHLY
Condition hair
Colour hair roots
Pedicure (summer)
Re-assess your diet
Examine breasts

2-MONTHLY
Trim hair

6-MONTHLY
Highlight hair
Visit gynaecologist
Explore a new interest
Have a 'day of beauty' or a weekend
  at a spa

gives a marvellous, temporary glow to the complexion. There are different types of masks, from gels to packs; choose one that is right for your skin type.

For dry skin, choose a peel-off mask. These do not cleanse as well as other types of masks but are gentle and effective for toning and stimulation.

For oily skin, try a clay mask.

For a special occasion, try a mask with menthol or camphor. After you apply the beauty mask to your face and neck, relax with your feet elevated for 15–20 minutes – it will do wonders for your circulation.

Caution When applying a mask, avoid the eye area.

Facials

You can benefit from a facial if your pores are clogged, your skin dry and your skin tone poor. A good facial

Often made from natural ingredients like bananas, oats and egg whites, face masks give a deep clean and leave your face clear and smooth. Apply cucumber to your eyes at the same time to help you relax and to eliminate puffiness.

enhances the effects of daily skin maintenance. It starts with the removal of make-up from the skin followed by massage and deep cleansing which includes manual extraction of blackheads and whiteheads. A salon facial 'vacuums' your pores, removes dead skin cells, moisturizes your skin and restores its natural balance. A steam facial, to open and cleanse the pores, can be done at home. A good time to give yourself a facial, or have one done professionally, is at the beginning of each season to remove the build-up of dead cells and environmental pollution.

Caution Steam facials are not recommended for women with delicate, sensitive skin or women with broken capillaries as they have been known to exacerbate these conditions.

SPECIAL TIPS

However well you look after your skin, some days it might need a boost. Try these ideas.

Broken capillaries Sensitive skin is prone to broken capillaries. Be gentle with your skin. Rough rubbing of the skin with a wash cloth may cause capillaries to break. Never use abrasives such as brushes or granules on the skin. Lessen the risk of broken capillaries by avoiding extremes of hot and cold water and use only luke-warm water when washing or bathing. Avoid saunas, extremes of temperature, spices and alcohol.

For a dewy look on hot summer days Apply ice-cold, thin slices of watermelon over your face and neck. If you have cucumber in the house, cut two thin slices and apply to closed eyes. Relax for 10 minutes, then remove.

To firm up eyelids and eliminate puffiness Open eyes wide. Stare straight ahead of you. Squeeze eyes tightly shut. Repeat six times, twice daily.

For sparkling, healthy eyes Soak cotton pads in tea or witch hazel. Lie down, apply to closed eyes and enjoy the soothing sensation for five to ten minutes. For a very special occasion, follow this with ice-cubes (wrapped in a cloth) over the entire eye area. Tap briskly but lightly around the eye area and feel the invigorating effect.

To minimize lines around nose and lip area Before starting, apply cream to neck, nose and mouth lines.

1 Looking straight ahead, purse your lips together to form a small 'o'.

2 Mouth the sound 'oooo'.

3 Open your mouth very wide — without causing discomfort — and mouth the word 'wow'.

4 Repeat 'oooo', 'wow' for a count of 25.

Do twice a day.

Watch the chinline

Cream the chinline by applying cream to throat in upward motion with both hands. Work the cream thoroughly into the skin; tissue off.

To firm chinline, apply cream to chin. Open mouth as wide as possible. Thrust lower lip up and out and try to reach nose. You can feel and see the muscles of the neck tightening. Do eight daily.

To maintain chinline, walk sit and stand 'tall', holding your neck up and keeping your chin level.

Wrinkle treatment

Retin-A is one of the most exciting wrinkle treatment products presently on the market. Available only by doctor's prescription, it is derived from Vitamin A. Results show after daily use for about a year — skin becomes smoother and tighter, lines become fewer and pigment spots fade. Treatment must be maintained or the skin reverts to its original condition.

Tip A wrinkle eraser — which is temporary but great for the morale! Take an egg yoke, beat well, add a tablespoon of olive oil. Apply mixture to face and allow it to remain for 15 minutes. Rinse off. *Voilà!*

THE BATH

For a deliciously soothing experience, there is nothing like a bath! And it not only feels good but is also a marvellous therapeutic treatment that relaxes tight muscles and releases tension. Step into a bathtub filled high with warm water, add a scented gel and lie back and savour the experience of total relaxation.

Keep smiling
Smiling is a great facial exercise! It makes you seem more friendly, gives a pleasant look to your face, and, according to research, even makes you feel better.

Beauty bath essentials

● Use warm, never very hot, water – hot water dries out the skin and very hot water can sometimes cause fainting.

● Time – the most necessary ingredient for the 'total experience'. Allow yourself about 10–15 undisturbed minutes.

● Use a long-handled bath brush, a face cloth, a natural sea sponge or a loofah, to gently abrade the skin, remove dead skin cells and improve circulation.

There is no better way to eliminate stress and fatigue than a luxurious soak in a herbal or sandalwood bath. Inhale the delicious aroma of your favourite fragrance. Finish the experience with a soft fleecy towel and a gentle application of your favourite lotion to keep your skin fragrant and soft.

● Soaps — try natural glycerine soaps which do not dry the skin, or exotic, scented soaps, some of which contain moisturizers.

Caution If you are taking vaso-constricting blood-pressure medication, or other prescribed medication, check with your doctor — bathing might not be for you.

Special note
● To make a herbal sachet, put a bit of your favourite herb in a muslin bag. Hang it over the hot water tap while the bath is running.
● Use a pumice stone for rough heels and elbows. Moisten it then rub it, in a circular motion, over elbows and heels.

FRAGRANCES
Fragrance can express your personality, create a mood. The aura of a certain fragrance can be your fashion signature, announce your presence, leave a lingering scent when you are gone. Great beauties, throughout history, have used perfume to express their personality or create a mood . . . romantic . . . seductive . . . intoxicating. Have you a scent that is uniquely yours? One that is in keeping with the image you wish to project? Why not consider trying something new?
For the sophisticated woman: an exotic scent, with ingredients from the Orient, such as jasmine, patchouli. Use scent to convey a mysterious mood. Examples: Opium (Yves St. Laurent); Obsession (Calvin Klein); Shalimar (Guerlain); KL (Parfums Lagerfeld); Fendi (Parfums Fendi); K. de Krizia (Krizia).

Treat yourself to a monthly body application of exfoliating cream. Applied to elbows, knees, legs, and other rough areas it leaves you feeling smoother and softer all over.

Did you know that . . .
. . . in ancient times Roman matrons filled their tubs with olive oil for smoother, softer skin?
. . . when Nero's wife was banished, legend has it that her only request was to be allowed to bring 60 horses with her so that she could continue to have her mare's milk baths? (Today's woman may occasionally imitate her sybaritic tendencies by adding a cupful of milk to the bath water to soothe and soften sensitive skin.)
. . . Darjeeling tea cools bath water and soothes a sunburn; chamomile tea in the bath helps insomnia, and jasmine tea in the bath just makes you feel good?

For the outdoor woman: a woodsy combination such as sandalwood, rosewood and cedar. The mood is natural and alive. Examples: Ivoire (Balmain); L'air du Temps (Nina Ricci); Caleche (Hermès).

For the romantic woman: mixed floral, subtly blended fragrances which are soft and unmistakably feminine. Examples: Anaïs Anaïs (Cacharell); Ombre Rose (Jean-Charles Broseau); Chloë (Parfums Lagerfeld).

For an old-fashioned effect – a single floral, rose or lilac.

For a natural effect – a fresh citrus blend comprising oranges, lemons, limes. Example: Eau Fraiche (Elizabeth Arden).

For the executive woman: crisp but understated classic blends such as Madame Rochas, or the more recent Knowing.

While your choice can be influenced by mood and personality, the determining factor is how the fragrance reacts with your body chemistry. Don't let your choice be based on whether you like the perfume on someone else; there is no way of knowing, until you try, how the same perfume will react on your skin.

Scent behind the ears is not enough! For an aura of fragrance wherever you go, spray on your wrists, behind your knees and add a dash of cologne to your hair.

Surround yourself and those you come close to with your favourite scent. Make an individual statement that lingers on long after you have left the room. Select perfumes, soaps, bath gels and pot pourri.

Special note
- If your skin is oily, use less perfume.
- The most efficient way to apply scent is with an atomizer.
- Don't keep your perfume forever. Perfume evaporates and changes scent with time.
- When you store perfume, never keep it in the sunlight, as it will lose its scent.
- If your favourite fragrance does not last on your skin, try using a scented bath gel or cream after your bath followed by a splash of perfume or eau de toilette (all in the same scent).

Caution Sunlight on perfumed skin can cause discolouration, irritation and attracts insects. Scent sprayed on jewellery or furs will discolour them.

ace and hands

MAKE-UP TECHNIQUES

Cosmetics, properly applied, can work magic. They can create the illusion of a more youthful face; a look of elegance or sophistication; and a look of glamour or drama. But the way we use make-up and the way we apply it has to change. It must change because the products have changed; because the right way to apply cosmetics has changed; and because we ourselves change. The secret is to keep up-to-date. If you are wearing the make-up that worked for you ten years ago, you need to update your look. Make-up styles have changed; make-up products have changed; *you* have changed.

> **T**HERE IS NO SUCH THING AS AN UGLY WOMAN – JUST A LAZY ONE.
>
> Elizabeth Arden

Make-up, properly applied, can make you look years younger, and it should be used to maximize your best features and camouflage flaws. Knowing which make-up products to use, and how to use is the first step in looking great.

MAKE-UP FOR YOUTH
● Take years off your eyes by applying eye make-up effectively. Opt for soft, subtle colours in eye shadow and use eye-fix primer to stop shadow going into

creases. Avoid irridescent eye shadows that accentuate fine lines around the eyes. An irridescent highlighter under the brows gives a droopy look to eyes. Liquid eyeliners create a harsh look; kohl pencils a heavy look. Opt for soft eye pencils or crayons, in natural tones of brown, grey or taupe.

● For 'laugh lines' on the outer corners of the eyes, use medium matt shadow on lid and crease, but not on the outer corners. Highlight brow bone with a pastel, like warm pink.

● For fine lines or wrinkles under the eye, avoid heavy make-up which emphasizes these lines. Use a slightly lighter foundation or a concealer in the eye area. Apply lightly and blend well.

● To de-emphasize a heavy jawline or to minimize a double chin, use a slightly darker shade of foundation along your jawline just under the bone; again, be sure to blend well.

● Apply lip-fix cream and use a pencil (the same colour as your lipstick) to outline your lips and to keep the lipstick from 'bleeding' into the fine lines around the mouth.

Right A look of natural beauty – understated, with the essential shadows redefined for the 1990s to look simple but attractive. The right products and colours skilfully applied are the keys to success.

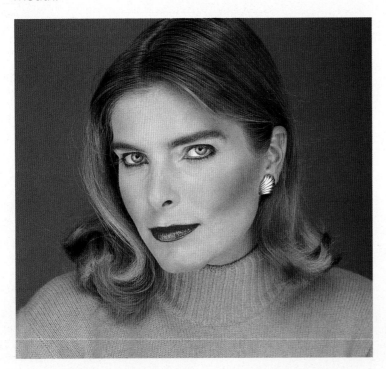

Left This dated look is caused by too-orange make-up unevenly applied, eyes too heavily lined, blusher applied without blending and silvery eye shadow which makes the eyes look hooded.

• Dust translucent powder lightly on your face, in downward strokes, to create a polished finish rather than a stiff, mask-like, look.

Make-up does not need to show to be effective. Avoid a harsh look by balancing your make-up. If you decide to emphasize your mouth with a bright shade of lipstick, use darker make-up on your eyes; if you decide to focus on your eyes, apply a positive shade of lipstick. The art of make-up is in the subtlety – the blending. Blend, blend, blend, for a more natural effect. Use subtle colours to co-ordinate with your clothes, to give you a well put together, harmonious look.

Special note
• To avoid irritation or infection from bacteria, remember to wash your hands before applying make-up and *never* share cosmetics with others.
• Discard old make-up. If a cream changes consistency or smells, throw it out. Never keep mascara more than four months.

THE PRODUCTS
Make sure you get the best out of cosmetic products by finding out exactly what is on offer, and how it works.

Moisturizers
Designed to seal in moisture they work best when applied to damp skin. They also help prevent the

1 Apply concealer to moisturized face covering blemishes, circles under eyes and creases around mouth.

2 Apply colour corrector sparingly to conceal redness.

3 Use a light mousse, which will not settle in creases, on face and eye area.

4 Soft-pink cream eye colour blends with violet in the corner to flatter the eyes.

5 Draw pencil eyeliner into the lashes and blend into corners of the bottom lash. Finish with blue/black mascara on lashes.

6 Lip liner pencil applied over lipfix defines lip shape and is filled in with bright tawny pink – darker on sides and lighter towards centre.

7 Soft peach/cream blusher lifted high into temples and contoured to forehead is set lightly with powder blush in same tone to give face a healthy glow.

7

4 5 6

foundation from being absorbed into the skin. Moisturizers are now available with built-in sun protection. Apply, leave on for 20 minutes so that it can be absorbed into the skin, then apply make-up.

Primers

Creams or liquids used under foundation to eliminate redness or yellowness in the complexion and create an even tone. If your complexion is red and blotchy, use green; if sallow, use purple; if extremely pale or greyish, use apricot. Apricot is also effective for black skin, 'warming' the skin and giving it a bright glow.

Concealers

Essential after 40, these conceal dark under-eye circles, obliterate small blemishes and skin discolorations and help reshape your features. Use a concealer a shade or two lighter than your skin, to 'light out' shadows under the eyes and around the nose or the lines at the side of the mouth.

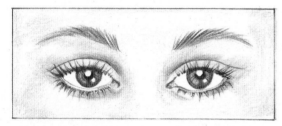

Close-set. Apply bright shadow diagonally beyond the outer edge. Use highlighter from inner corner of eye upwards to brow. Use mascara on outer lashes.

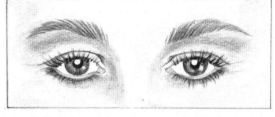

Deep set eyes. Choose pale or smoky shades of shadow. Apply above crease line and blend upwards and out.

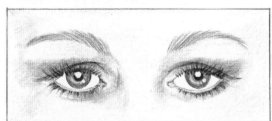

Hooded eyes. Apply dark smoky shadows to crease line, blend towards browbone. Use a pale colour on lids near to lashes and blend outward. Apply mascara especially to corners.

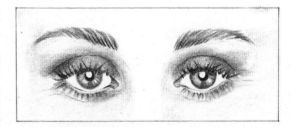

Prominent eyes. Use dark smoky shadow on eyeline and even darker in the crease line. Pencil upper and lower lids close to lashes. Apply heavy mascara to lashes.

Foundation

This improves the skin's texture and gives it an even-toned finish. Choose a foundation colour as close to your skin colour as possible to achieve a natural look. A too dark foundation colour is ageing.

Apply either with fingers or a small sponge. A sponge is particularly good for applying foundation to the difficult area around the nose. Be sure to blend it evenly into the hairline and below the chin, so that there will be no sharp line where the make-up stops.

Blushers

These liven up a dull complexion and add vitality to the face, making it seem more vivacious. They come in powder, cream, or liquid form and can be applied with a brush, a damp sponge or fingertips. Liquid blusher works well for dry or mature skin but is difficult to apply. Shimmery blushers are only for flawless complexions.

The key to using blusher effectively is to blend, blend, blend. Harsh strokes of colours are dated.

Eye shadow

Eye shadows come in powders or creams. Powdered shadows create a softer effect and require more application of colour. Avoid gels and frosted or shiny shadows as they draw attention to tiny wrinkles and laugh lines. Avoid gels as they melt into creases and accentuate lines. Do not date yourself by matching your eye shadow to your clothes, or to the colour of your eyes.

Cream shadow works on dry skin but must be applied sparingly and blended to avoid an uneven effect.

Eye liner

Liner makes the lashes appear fuller. Shades such as charcoal, grey and brown give the most natural look.

Apply subtly, with a soft eye pencil, eye crayon or a fine-tipped sable brush. When applying an eye pencil or crayon, use one soft enough to glide across your lid without pulling. Be gentle to avoid pulling the fragile skin area around your eye. For maximum soft effect, smudge the liner above and below the lash line.

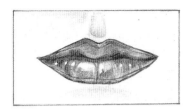

Thin lips. Use a lip pencil darker than your lipstick and draw above and below the natural lip line as required. Fill in with pencil and bright lipstick, then blend.

Thin top lip. As for thin lips adjusting top lip shape only.

Droopy lips. Outline your lower lip with a pencil so that it goes up at the edges. Use a lighter shade on the top lip and add gloss to centre.

Uneven lips. Use a lip pencil to even up the sides. Start at the outer corner and work inwards.

Mascara

This accentuates the eyes and gives them depth and dimension.

Conditioning mascara works for dry, brittle lashes. It softens the lashes and gives a natural effect. Don't use them if you rub your eyes as it can smudge easily.

Lash-building mascara contains fine hair fibres which thicken and lengthen lashes. Because this type of mascara can flake, it is not recommended for sensitive eyes or for contact lens wearers.

Waterproof mascara does not flake, stays on longer and can be worn when swimming.

After applying *mascara*, use a lash comb to separate lashes. Too many coats also make the lashes appear spiky and unnatural. Remove with make-up remover.

Lash tinting

A process which temporarily darkens your lashes in the shade of your choice. It is good for blondes with very fair lashes, for redheads with gingery lashes, for women with dark lashes but fair tips. If done well, the effect is attractive and natural. Mascara can be used afterwards to thicken the lashes. The tint will fade out in four to six weeks. If you decide to have it done, make sure to choose a meticulous specialist. It's not for those who are allergic or tend to have eye infections.

Brow tinting is also available at most hair salons. If you dye your hair lighter, consider matching your brows.

Lipstick

If you want to add sparkle or vitality to your face, wear lipstick. Because lipstick often turns bluish on the mouth, test the shade on your hand before buying. Gloss applied over lipstick causes the colour to smudge.

To make lipstick stay on longer, dust mouth with powder before applying lipstick. To keep your lipstick from smearing or running into the fine lines around your lips, use lip fix creme.

Lip pencil

This prevents lipstick from bleeding into the tiny wrinkles

If your lips are your best feature, draw attention to them by adding a glow of colour to the centre of your mouth. You will need outliner colour and a lighter lipstick colour. Outline your lips in the darker colour, fill in upper lip with dark colour; then do the lower lip, but do not fill in the centre. Apply the lighter colour to the centre of the lower. *Voilà* – a sensuous mouth!

around the mouth and creates a clean, neat look. Match the pencil colour to your lipstick shade.

Powder

This sets the foundation and takes away the shine that is flattering only to a young face. The new sheer translucent powders help conceal pores, give a matt finish to the face, and add the finishing touch to your make-up. For sensitive skin, choose fragrance-free powder; for dry skin, try a moisture-enriched one. Loose powder is preferable to solid, compressed powder. Tinted powder can 'warm up' your complexion but gives a powdered look that is unflattering for day wear.

To avoid an artificial, mask-like look, apply sparingly. Dip a big, fluffy brush into your loose powder, shake off excess, then whisk evenly all over your face. For a 'natural glow' take a cotton ball, dip it into cold water or astringent, squeeze out excess moisture, and pat gently over face, omitting the nose area.

TOOLS OF THE TRADE

Start with a good set of brushes. Brushes make it possible to create a more professional, polished finish. Use brushes to blend colour from a subtle daytime look to a more exciting evening look. Treat yourself to sable brushes – they last longer and work better. You'll need:
- a big, round fluffy brush for dusting on loose powder
- a smaller round, fluffy brush for applying blusher
- a small, point-tipped brush for painting on eyeliner
- a small stiff brush to shape eyebrows
- a tiny comb or a wiry spiral brush to separate lashes after applying mascara

Cosmetic basics

- moisturizer • concealer • foundation • translucent powder; pressed powder • blusher • eye make-up: mascara, shadow, eye pencils, highlighter • lipstick, lip pencil • cotton balls, Q-tips.

Options eyelash curler; small sponges to be used for applying moisturizer, foundation or blusher; primer.

Brunettes look best in vibrant colours, especially in tones of red and blue. Choose lipsticks in cherry red, burgundy or mauvy pinks and match your blusher to lipstick in tone. Foundations should be cool beiges which match your skin colour on the chin. Eye colours should be smoky from mauve to blue/grey.

Beige, peach or ivory foundations are generally suitable for blondes. Eye colours in neutral, taupe and tawny shades look natural. Lip and cheek colours are best kept soft in pinky rose or brighter coral. Although shades of icy pastels most compliment the delicate complexion of this cool blonde, she would also look striking and radiant in cherry red, mauve and French navy. Don't be afraid to ring the changes, matching your make-up to the look you wish to project.

Redheads look best in earthy or russet tones of eye colour with light brown or coral lip and cheek colour. If your complexion is ruddy, wear concealer to even the tone.

Warmer shades of foundation are a good choice for you. Here, we used a warm beige foundation to cover a slightly freckled complexion. Soft coral blusher, and smudgy green/ gold shadows accentuate her feline hazel eyes and coordinate with the gold velour sweater.

If your skin is very pale, use a peach or mauve colour corrector to warm it up. A light foundation mousse gives a natural look. Choose soft shell-pink, mauve or blue/grey eye colours and use a deep rose lip pencil with pinky rose lipstick on the mouth. This look is soft and feminine but women with this colouring can also look dynamic in a stronger palate of hot pink, blue-reds and navy.

Black skin looks good with a quite sheer foundation in a colour that matches your skin. Highlight with smoky grey/black or grey/navy – or with bright shades of red for an exciting look. Here, we paid special attention to the uneven complexion, in particular the dark tones around mouth and laugh lines. We have livened up her skin tone with a peachy-pink blush and added a luscious red mouth to emphasize her attractive colouring.

Essentials for skin maintenance
● cleanser (cream or cleansing bar) ● exfoliating lotion ●
eye make-up remover ● lubricating cream ● eye cream ●
lip moisturizer ● cuticle cream ● hand cream ● body lotion
● sun screen ● tweezers ● special throat cream

Make-up basics for day
2 lipsticks ● foundation ● translucent powder, pressed
powder ● blusher ● eye shadow palette ● eye pencil ● lip
pencil ● 2 mascaras – one black, one in colour ● lip fix
creme ● lipbrush ● comb ● mirror ● elastic band ● 2 safety
pins

Contents of evening bag
lipstick ● lip pencil ● lip brush ● lipfix ● powder compact ●
comb ● mirror ● elastic band ● safety pins

FOR YOUNG-LOOKING HANDS
Beautiful hands are a showcase for jewellery and are
always on display: when you eat, write, or apply your
lipstick. Look after your hands as you would your
complexion. Prevent 'old-looking' hands by applying a
moisturizing cream after washing. Apply it while your
hands are still damp, so that the moisturizer can seal in
the water. Add a good sun screen when going outdoors
in the sun. Lined rubber gloves when washing the dishes
and cotton gloves for household chores will save your
hands and get into the habit of frequently and lavishly
pampering your hands with lotion. Every now and then
try a warm paraffin dip to remove dead skin and soften
calluses.

If you have brown spots on your hands, and want to
bleach them out, ask your doctor to prescribe a good
fade-out cream. A prescription fade-out cream works
better than the bleaching creams sold over the counter.

NAILS
Cared-for nails are noticed and are very much a part of
the total look you project. Are yours cared for or
neglected? Chipped nail polish and broken nails convey
a neglected appearance. Rings and bracelets draw

Well cared for hands and nails
provide a sophisticated finish to
your look. Try something new:
paint crimson 'v' shapes over a
silvery base and for that special
occasion add a subtle glitter to
the corners of your little fingers.

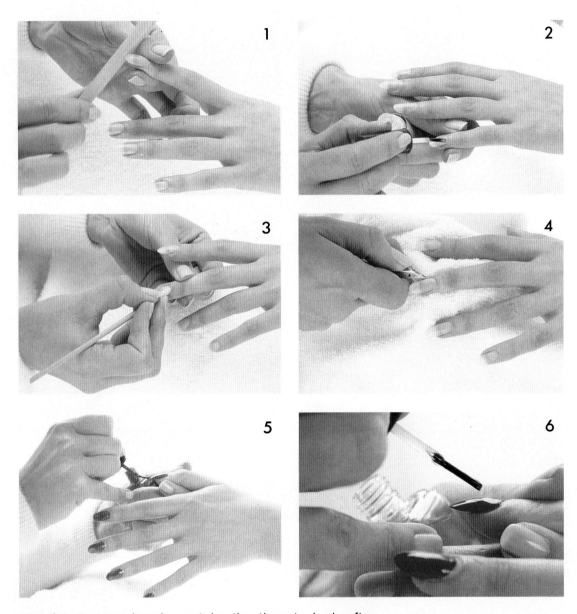

attention to your hands so take the time to look after them. For very special evenings, indulge in beautiful painted nails by using silver and red polish to create V shapes and crescent shaped motifs.

The manicure
A professional manicure should stay looking good for at least a week. Too many coats of polish can cause nail polish to peel. To make a manicure last longer, add a

1 Make sure that all polish is removed and that your nails are clean before you begin to shape them. Use a smooth emery board to file into the desired shape.

2 Apply cuticle remover to sides of nail and smooth into nail pushing back cuticles to help soften them. Soak your fingers in a small glass bowl full of lukewarm water to soften the skin.

3 Wrap an orange stick with cotton wool and push back cuticles gently so that they stand away from the nail.

4 Using a cuticle cutter, gently remove hangnails being careful not to prick the skin as this can cause infection.

5 After applying handcream, massage in circular strokes. Remove from nails by rinsing fingers. Apply base coat.

6 Apply varnish to each nail in two even strokes. You can try painting 'v's or paint leaving the crescent bare. Allow the first coat to dry before applying the top coat.

thin layer of top coat every second day, putting a bit under the nail edge to help prevent chipping.

Special note
● Calluses and hangnails? Try daily moisturizing with cuticle cream.
● Chipped polish? Use a pencil or pen when dialling the phone.
● Split nails? Are you using a harsh emery board or filing both ways?
● Brittle nails? You may lack Vitamin A or calcium. Check your diet.
● Still biting your nails? Consider a hypnotist.

Sculptured nails cover broken nails and lengthen short nails. Nails are sculptured by placing shape-making forms under tips while acrylic solution is brushed over nails to build and extend them.

Wrappings are used to mend damaged nails and strengthen weak ones. A swatch of silk, cotton, linen, paper or cellophane is glued to the top of the nail. After the glue dries, the nail is buffed. To avoid infection, the wrap should never extend to the cuticle – that is when problems are likely to occur.

Nail tips are glued and can be covered by silk, linen or an acrylic solution. An application of glue is applied after which nails are buffed and filed. Touch-ups are required every two to three weeks to keep your hands looking at their absolute best.

There are three problems with artificial nails: allergy, infection and irritation. If a small opening forms between the natural nail and the artificial nail, dip your finger in alcohol before having the nail reglued. Women with a history of cosmetic allergies, or who tend to have skin or nail infections or warts on the skin around the nails, should avoid artificial nails.

While it's nice to have your nails pampered by a professional, you can take care of problem nails at home. Nail mender kits are inexpensive and relatively easy to use.

air

CARE · STYLES · LOOKS

One of the best things you can do for your hair as you get older is to experiment with a new cut or colour. Dare to change! Change your hairdresser; change your look. Consult a hair colorist; discuss adding highlights or lowlights to add a touch of class to your look.

Go to a top hairdresser and invest in a great cut. A good cut can almost take care of itself and will save you hours of fussing with your hair. An elaborate style that takes more than five minutes to arrange has no place in today's busy lifestyle. A good hairdresser will take into consideration the shape of your face, your height, your age, and most importantly, the thickness and texture of your hair. What he or she probably will *not* take into consideration is the way you dress or the image you wish to project. It is up to you to make sure the final look is suitable for your lifestyle.

Discuss the image you want to project. If you have a professional career, but the image you choose for your lifestyle is sensuous, ask how the same hairstyle can work for two different looks. If you have invested a

HAIRSTYLE, CUT AND COLOUR SHOULD BE DICTATED FROM WITHIN NOT BY FASHION OR TRENDS. A WOMAN WHO PROJECTS A LOOK OF ELEGANT SIMPLICITY CANNOT GO WRONG.

Michaeljohn

Above An upward sweep lifts the features and makes the face slimmer and more youthful. *Below* This smoothly pulled back style creates an elegant, sophisticated look for a more formal occasion.

fortune in Chanel-type clothing and want to finish your look with a style that is marvellous with that look (a one-length bob or your hair pulled back in a Chanel style with a bow), ask if your face shape is right for that style.

A safe bet for most women as they get older is either short or medium length hair in a soft, upswept style. This leads the eye upward and gives a more youthful appearance. If you like the youthful look of short hair but don't want a masculine look, keep your hair short at the nape but have the shape undefined to avoid the harsh edges often seen in boyish cuts. If you want to look more youthful and hate your present style, explore options with your hairdresser.

If you are sensitive about a facial flaw, ask for a style that will camouflage it. To draw attention away from the lower part of your face, ask for a hairstyle that will lead the eye upward. If you have deep forehead lines, hide them with a fringe (bangs). If you have just a few lines that you would like to disguise, a few strategically placed wisps pulled down onto the forehead will do the trick.

STYLING

If your hair is thin, and you want to make it appear fuller, try a mousse. Apply it to the roots of wet hair, style with fingers or brush and blow-dry. Use sparingly, as it can damage and dry the hair.

You can add weight and body to the hair with a styling gel but be aware that it makes hair look wet and appear darker. Gel helps hold the set and works well with coarse hair. A water-based gel is preferable to one with an oil base.

The hair sprays of today are a big improvement on the sprays of yesterday. But don't overdo them – they work best in moderation. Before shampooing, gently brush out spray. Try to avoid extra-hold sprays and sprays with a high alcohol content.

HAIR COLOUR

Do blondes have more fun? Why not find out! Or would you prefer a more conservative look ... one with lowlights to give your hair a rich warm colour? Or if you have freckles, have you thought about being a redhead? What suited you before may not become you now. Skin tones change with age. As a brunette of 20, perhaps you admired that Scandinavian blonde look but never thought it could be you. Think again, at this stage of your life, it may be flattering.

Hair colour is one of the easiest features to change and improve and can make the most dramatic difference in your appearance. A change from dark brown hair to brown with blonde highlights or from mousy grey to strawberry blonde can create a younger and more glamorous image. If you are undecided or not ready to make a commitment, experiment with rinses or semi-permanent hair colours. A semi-permanent colour washes out in six to eight shampoos, blends in grey hair and adds shine to dull hair. To play it safe, only lighten your colour one or two shades. Always go lighter, never darker: darker is ageing. Remember, grey or salt-and-pepper hair are also options.

Highlighting (sunbursting, painting, streaking)

Highlights lighten and brighten the hair and if done correctly it will look soft and natural. The process involves bleaching strands of hair in various shades of colour. The most important factor for successful highlighting is the placement and number of streaks. For best results, have it done at a salon.

For the mature face . . . place highlights all around the face for a softer look and to de-emphasize wrinkles.

For the round face . . . draw the eye upward by placing the streaks along the crown and at the temples.

For the thin face . . . place the highlights at the sides, near the hairline and going outward.

For the drooping face . . . create a 'halo' of colour from temple to temple by placing highlights on hair ends.

To de-emphasize jowls or a double chin . . . place streaks along the crown and at the temples.

Lowlighting

Lowlighting is a subtle way of adding warmth and

To Colour or Not to Colour
- Yes, if you become grey very early and are not comfortable with it
- Yes, if you need to project a young image in your professional field
- Yes if you want to change the image you project
- Yes, if you just feel the need for a change

Highlighting is for you if:
- Your hair is beginning to get grey and you want to conceal it or to create a softer look
- You have light to medium-brown hair
- You don't want a drastic change
- You want to add a touch of glamour to your hair
- You want to create the illusion of a more perfect face shape

richness to your hair. Strands of red and brown are blended to add reddish brown lowlights. It is particularly flattering to women with red or auburn hair.

Grey hair

Grey hair is the new colour of the 90s for the woman who is secure in who she is. Barbara Bush has become a role model for women who choose not to change their hair colour. Christian Lacroix's top model, Marie Seznec, is popular largely because of her striking salt-and-pepper hair. More women are opting for grey hair and looking for ways to make it look more attractive.

If you decide to keep your hair grey, re-assess your hair care. Grey hair tends to be very dry as hormone levels in the body decrease with age. Conditioners now need to be part of your hair routine. Protect your hair from the sun with a scarf or hat as the sun can lighten and change the colour. If your hair has unflattering blue or brassy tones, eliminate them with a colour wash or rinse. To lift the yellow and enhance the grey tone, have a professional salon strip the yellow cast with a lightener

Let your hair go grey the natural way! Or, add highlights to merge grey and blonde for a flattering, quality look.

or do it yourself with a semi-permanent, grey-enhancing home colouring kit that does not contain peroxide. Use a shampoo especially designed for grey hair.

Grey hair can be great hair but it needs to be worn with the right make-up. Use muted eye colours, avoiding black eye liners and mascaras. Lipstick colours should be soft and light, in coral pinks or soft peaches rather than dark reds or fuchsias.

Salt and pepper hair

This is very striking and can be very becoming. If you like a softer effect have your hairdresser add highlights, with more emphasis on the front.

PERMING OR STRAIGHTENING

If you decide to perm or straighten your hair, make sure you understand what is involved.

Permed hair

Most perms last at least three or four months. If your hair loses its bounce before then, trim it. A perm will

A cropped salt and pepper look is casual and very attractive. Sophisticated, but also youthful, it's a style that will take you from day to evening and from office to opera house with equal ease.

usually survive three trims. Never perm your hair the same time you colour it, it's damaging. Make sure the hair dye you use is safe for permed hair.

Straightened hair

This process dries the hair and requires maintenance. The hair roots usually require touch-ups every few months. Straightened hair needs a lot of conditioning plus the occasional hot-oil treatment.

HAIR CARE FOR HEALTHY HAIR

Whatever style you choose for your hair it will look at its best if your hair is healthy. Treat your hair with respect and it will reward you with a vibrant glow.

Shampooing and conditioning

Frequent washing is good for the hair. Like the skin, hair needs water, followed by conditioners to help seal in the moisture. Because clean hair looks thicker and appears to have more volume, gentle shampooing (with light fingertip movements) is especially helpful for fine or thin hair. Fine hair needs conditioner for more body but requires very thorough rinsing to avoid limpness. Thick, coarse hair absorbs shampoo and needs very thorough rinsing; conditioners benefit it by making it more manageable and giving it shine.

Special note

• Know your hair type and select the shampoo that suits your hair type best. Alternate between two brands of shampoos for best results.
• Make conditioners part of your hair regime

Brushing

Brushing your hair can be damaging. Brushing wet hair can cause it to break. Strong brushing can cause some hair loss. The type of brush you use can effect the condition of your hair. The best brushes are those with very soft natural long bristles or soft ones with long plastic bristles that bend easily. Avoid a short bristled brush, one with metal prongs and metal combs.

Setting

Hair rollers, used to excess, also cause hair breakage. Never sleep with hair rollers — the strain on your hair is too great. Use hot hair rollers for 'emergencies' only — they are extremely drying and damaging to the hair.

Drying

Avoid overdrying! Drying the hair from wet to damp does not harm the hair — overdrying does. The damage usually occurs during the last few minutes. Avoid this and you will avoid split ends.

Combs, hairclips, bows and headbands enable you to make changes to a basic hairstyle. Try luxurious black velvet for evening or, for that tropical holiday, a bunch of grapes caught up in a chignon.

Cosmetic surgery

OPTIONS · ALTERNATIVES

There comes a time in life when a woman looks in the mirror and does not like what she sees. She sees a face that does not fit in with her own self-image, a face that looks older or 'tired'. She notices signs of ageing that she hadn't seen before . . . a few wrinkles, lines around the eyes, a jaw line that has begun to sag. Something has to be changed. Is it possible to slow down the biological clock? Is plastic surgery the answer? Are there alternatives?

You are a good candidate for plastic surgery if:
- You are in good health
- You are doing it for yourself, not for others
- You discuss with the surgeon what you want and what you can expect from the operation.
- You ask about possible complications and if and how they can be corrected.

You can expect to be terribly disappointed if:
- You feel that the surgery will 'change your life,'

> **M**AKE SURE YOUR EXPECTATIONS ARE REALISTIC AND YOUR PRIMARY MOTIVATING FACTOR COMES FROM WITHIN RATHER THAN FROM AN EXTERNAL SOURCE.
>
> Dr Harvey M. Rosen, M.D., D.M.D.

improve your relationships or make you a 'new person'.

● You go to a 'renowned plastic surgeon' who has been written up in popular magazines and appeared on talk shows, without checking his credentials with his peers.

WHAT PLASTIC SURGERY CAN DO

Face lifts, brow lifts, eyelidplasties, nasal contouring surgery, breast enlargement, breast lifting and liposuction are among the many operations undertaken. For more dramatic change, the facial balance and proportion of the face can be changed by enlarging the cheek bone or changing the shape and size of the lower jaw.

Today, advanced medical techniques mean that there are alternatives to major surgery when it comes to acquiring the perfect look. Some of these are mentioned below but remember, while cosmetic surgery is relatively safe, it is surgery and there is always the possibility of serious complications: nerve paralysis, excessive scarring, infection, bleeding.

Collagen injections Collagen injections are useful for filling in small areas of wrinkling on the face. Although it is a relatively simple procedure, the results are definitely temporary, lasting only about four to six months. Caution: some patients may have an allergic reaction; skin testing is done to determine allergic possibilities, but may not be totally reliable.

Fat injections If you are allergic to collagen injections, you might have considered fat injections. In this procedure, fat is removed from one part of the body and injected into another part of the body. However, fat is difficult to work with, and too heavy for fine wrinkles.

Silicone injections These are not recommended, except in unusual circumstances, because of their potential for complications. They are considered an experimental procedure by the American Food and Drug Administration.

Liposuction In this procedure, the plastic surgeon uses a very thin transparent hose to vacuum out the fat, which flows through the hose into a small canister on the floor. Caution: Before undergoing liposuction, check out your surgeon's experience and results with this procedure. A surgeon in the United States can obtain a certificate to perform liposuction after a weekend training period.

Laser surgery (as it relates to cosmetic surgery)
It is primarily done to lighten vascular birthmarks. Theoretically, its advantage is that it minimizes the scarring that can occur with other forms of surgical correction. But it is not without risk or complications.

ALTERNATIVES TO PLASTIC SURGERY

If you are nervous about undergoing any form of surgery but long to make 'minor adjustments' to your features, try cosmetics or exercise techniques.

Cover-up creams A wide variety of cover-up products, suitable for concealing broken capillaries, purple bruises, and other skin problems are now available. Some come in a convenient stick or crayon form. Others claim to cling to the skin, even adhering to scar tissue. Thick, opaque liquid products are suitable for covering discolourations, some are specifically designed for covering large areas of skin, especially good for concealing varicose veins.

Make-up techniques The new trend is to 'plump up the lips' with collagen. An alternative is to create the illusion of a fuller lip with a lip pencil. Outline the shape of the mouth keeping the pencil slightly above the natural lip line. Fill in with matching lipstick colour.

Facial exercises Facial exercises tone up the skin and increase blood circulation. Women who do these exercises and see good results claim it makes them look years younger, others claim that they do more harm than good. Most cosmetic surgeons believe 'facial exercises will not delay the effects of ageing on the face.' If facial exercises are part of your routine, be sure to apply a rich cream to the specific areas you are working on, especially the throat area.

Acupuncture or acupressure face lifts

As with facial exercises, some women say the effects are beneficial. Currently, there is no objective medical evidence to support the claim that they alleviate or delay the ageing process in the face or elsewhere in the body.

> HAVE IT DONE WHEN YOU ARE IN EXCELLENT HEALTH AND WITH A PROPER EMOTIONAL ATTITUDE. BECOME AS INFORMED AS POSSIBLE ABOUT THE SURGEON AND ABOUT THE OPERATION.
>
> Dr R. Barrett Noone, M.D.,

DENTAL COSMETICS

'Smile, please!' As the flashbulbs pop, some people grin from ear to ear while others barely smile. If you're one of those who hate to smile because your teeth are chipped and discoloured, don't be discouraged, there are new techniques available that can make them picture-perfect.

Bleaching Is done by applying peroxide solution to stained teeth. This technique might require several visits to the dentist before complete results. Some stains, however, such as those caused by consuming antibiotic tetracycline in childhood, may not be removable.

Bonding corrects the shape and colour of teeth through the application of tooth-coloured dental plastics. The technique covers stains completely, rebuilds cracked or chipped teeth, closes gaps, and builds up old, eroded teeth to make them look younger. Bonding can be done with one visit to the dentist, and with proper care can last up to five years. It is not a cure-all but suitable in certain cases.

Laminate veneers are thin layers of plastic or porcelain that are bonded to the surface of the tooth for cosmetic purposes. Some cases require the tooth enamel to be partly removed, but the process is usually safe. This technique requires multiple visits to the dentist, but the effects last much longer than regular bonding.

Caution

Discuss with your dentist the cost, durability and appearance of each of these procedures to find out which is best for you.

Implants An implant is a false tooth, in the form of a metal stump, which is inserted into the jaw bone and then crowned. It is a possible alternative to wearing dentures.

Dental fear If you are one of the many who avoid dental treatment through fear, there are strategies available to help you overcome this including relaxation techniques, and specific dental phobia treatment.

Cosmetic tip
A pleasant smile and white teeth are very much a part of today's culture. Use the right shade of lipstick to create an illusion of whiter teeth. Cool shades of lipstick make stained or yellowish teeth look whiter, while warm colours of lipstick, such as orange or brown-red emphasize the discolouration.

Clothes

COLOUR · TEXTURE · FABRIC · LIFESTYLE

When fashion designers create a collection they think in terms of colour, fabric and texture. They use colour as the ribbon that ties together the theme of the collection, but fabric and texture generally come first. Fabric and texture will determine whether the mood will be casual, sporty or formal. Soft wools are more suitable for day clothes while satins or silks lend themselves to an after-five look. The way fabric and colour work together determines whether an outfit looks cheap or expensive; the same red dress can look dull in polyester, stunning in silk.

> GOOD TASTE IN CLOTHES HAS NO
> BOUNDS. IT EMBODIES SIMPLICITY, LUXURY,
> HARMONY AND REFINEMENT.
>
> Chanel

COLOUR

How bland the world would be without colour! Colour has strong associations for us . . . the yellow of the golden sun, the azure blue of the ocean, the lush green of the grass. How boring clothing would be without it. Use colour in your clothing to project a mood; to create an effect.

Black . . . teamed with white can be used to make an impact or to create a high power look. Teamed with either red or yellow, it produces an exciting look.

Red . . . stands out in a crowd; wear it when you want to be noticed. Use it as an accent to make white look crisp, or with navy to create a nautical look. For a startling effect, team it with hot pink.

White . . . evokes 'presence'; make an entrance in winter-white at any time of the year. Try a white suit, white wool trousers with matching sweater, the softer the texture, the softer the aura. Cream satin, the height of luxury, brings out the starkness of a dull grey or light brown outfit. Team it with black velvet for drama.

Blue . . . everyone likes blue. Navy, the colour of spring. Create interesting combinations with it . . . accent it with green, top it with yellow, dot it with white, stripe it with red. Royal blue creates excitement as a bright accent for brown, black or white, in a brilliant scarf, held together with a golden clasp.

Icy pink . . . soft, inviting and cosy when worn with sandy-brown; expensive when teamed with off-white.

Hot pink or fuschia! . . . the perfect co-ordinating colour for dark navy or black.

Forest green . . . perfect for checks (plaids), striking with red, collegiate with navy.

Taupe . . . marvellous tone on tone, from light to dark, and finish with black, white or, in spring, with red.

Brown . . . unusual when combined with navy, cream or beige; beautiful tone on tone, from the palest shade of brown to the darkest bark; and in all brown, with a streak of coral — magnificent!

Yellow . . . dramatic with black, happy with blue, bold with red.

TEXTURE

Notice the crispness of cotton, the slippery cool feel of satin, the softness of cashmere and mix textures to create different effects. Mixing the rough with the smooth, mixing fabric and texture creates excitement and evokes different moods:

Richness . . . velvet and satin

Opulence . . . velour and taffeta

Simplicity . . . organdy and flannel

Luxury (day) . . . tweed and cashmere

Luxury (evening) . . metallic lamés with moire
Primness . . . jersey knit with wool flannel
Romance . . . lace and satin
Femininity . . . angora with wool worsted
French look . . . flannel and foulard silks
Laura Ashley/Gibson Girl . . . cotton knit with gaberdine

PATTERN

Pattern provides yet another dimension to the design of an outfit. The variety of patterns is endless and exciting and while teaming up two patterns can be tricky, there are some great combinations:

● Narrow stripes can be worn with wider stripes of the same colour. Use this to make a bold fashion statement.
● Stripes can be combined with polka dots – in the same colour. for example, a black and white striped suit looks great with a black and white polka-dot shirt.
● Paisley teamed with tapestry or tweeds in harmonious colours is a good combination.
● Combine paisley and brocade with a solid satin to create an expensive evening look.
● Combine tweed and fairisle with check (plaid) in colours that blend well for a casual country look.
● A border print is effective with a small all-over floral in the same colour scheme.
● Small houndstooth can work with large houndstooth or with a floral pattern. For example, choose a scarf with houndstooth centre and floral border.

FABRIC

The look wear and feel of a fabric determines the mood; a different fabric can transform the same garment from sporty to dressy, from cheap to expensive. A nubby tweed suit will not look or feel like a silk suit, nor will the wear be the same. Wool creates a casual look, silk a more formal mood. To project the look you wish, you need to know something about fabrics.

Natural fabrics

Natural fabrics look rich and feel rich. They are always recommended for a look of quality. A marvellous silk blouse, a good cashmere sweater, fine wool slacks always looks timeless and classic. Natural fabrics not only look great, they 'breathe', and they are more durable. Unfortunately, they require time and care. Silks and cashmeres are best cleaned; cotton and linen need to be ironed. Although silks can be washed at home, they require special attention. Natural fabrics are more expensive and you may find they do not work for your way of life.

Silk . . . is the most elegant of all the natural fibres and is always in good taste. Silk adds glamour to day or evening dress, drapes beautifully, teams well with wool, velvet and other fabrics.

Linen . . . good linen always looks rich. It is the perfect look for spring and summer; it is cool and it is chic. Unfortunately, it creases easily and requires maintenance.

Cotton . . . is cool, crisp and comfortable. It is 'a must' in extreme heat and in cooler weather it is the perfect layer under a sweater. It moves easily with the body and can be starched to look crisp.

Wool . . . the comfort and quality look of wool cannot be duplicated. Wools range from fine wool worsteds to wool crêpes and vary in thickness and weave. They lend themselves to interesting and subtle textures and can be casual or dressy. Wool crêpe is particularly fine and elegant.

Synthetic blends

Some synthetic blends are a great alternative to natural fabrics. They are ideal if you travel a lot and need wrinkle-resistant fabrics or if you are on a tight budget and cannot afford either the initial investment of natural fabrics or the dry cleaning bills.

Fabric blends, when made well, can combine the quality look of natural fabrics with the easy-care conveniences of synthetics. A good combination of wool and polyester can look great, feel good and not wrinkle easily. The best blends have a higher natural fabric content than synthetics: a good ratio is 60% natural fabric, 40% synthetic.

General tips for all lifestyles

- Look for comfortable, attractive clothes that you can wear with pleasure and total confidence; choose good quality, well-designed clothes for maximum use, year after year.
- Buy the best you can afford for the key items.
- Make sure you are appropriately dressed for the occasion and the situation.
- Project a more finished image by matching your tights or stockings to your skirt and shoes. Tone on tone always looks right. Contrasting colours in hose and shoes shorten the leg.
- Don't overlook the obvious. Never wear spotted or wrinkled clothes.

Here are the looks and how to achieve them:

Every woman needs a perfect white blouse to provide a pivot for the outfits in her wardrobe. Teamed with skirts and trousers, it can be dressed up or down to work for just about any occasion.

Choose separates that look good together for an infinitely flexible wardrobe. With a t-shirt for casual and belted for a smart look, this safari jacket is easy and comfortable for both town and country. Its neutral tone works well with red, black, navy and olive, making it an excellent basic for everyone's wardrobe.

A chic, tailored look that can be duplicated whatever your budget. This vibrant cherry red jacket teamed with a multicolour green skirt makes a positive fashion statement, especially smart when worn with an elegant foulard print scarf.

Above Whether catching up on the *Financial Times* or preparing for a client's meeting, this easy, unadorned double-breasted suit is right for all business occasions.

Opposite It's not the real thing but it's a great copy! Accessorized with lots of chains and pearls, it's a must for every woman's wardrobe.

Above Create that Grace Kelly feeling in a sweeping chiffon skirt teamed with a velvet embossed jacket in the most flattering coral colour – guaranteed to make every woman feel and look romantic.

Opposite The little black dress may look basic under a jacket for work but it can carry through to the evening, making a daring, sensuous statement with its plunging low back.

BASIC WARDROBE

You don't need a lot of clothes in your wardrobe to look great. A basic wardrobe consists of classic separate pieces that are colour co-ordinated in such a way that they can be worn on their own or with other separates to gain more mileage and flexibility from your clothes.

The motto is, quality, not quantity. A few beautiful, functional, wearable outfits will take you everywhere you need to go and give the impression of an overflowing wardrobe. Avoid the latest trends and go instead for style. Find a fabulous handbag that you can wear for years, a smart up-to-date belt that will give this year's look to last year's suit. Go for quality!

Here are the 14 pieces of clothing you need for a basic wardrobe:

● one skirt suit (counts as two pieces) ● one trouser suit (counts as two pieces) ● one blazer ● one skirt ● one dress ● 3 blouses, one tie style, one collarless, one lapel ● one coat ● 3 sweaters, one polo neck, one cardigan style, one cable knit.

To make this work effectively, base your wardrobe around a three-colour scheme. Use the dominant colour for the major pieces (coat, suits, trousers) and two other colours for the smaller items (sweaters, blouses, scarves, accessories). Do not be tempted beyond the three colours. Choose solids, not prints and make sure the colours are flattering to you.

Mix and match

There is infinite mileage in a 14-piece wardrobe. Here are 10 different outfits without even trying!

● Team the polo neck sweater with a matching skirt and top with same or different colour cardigan as an alternative to a stiff suit for that in-between occasion.

● Team one suit jacket (black) with houndstooth skirt and red shirt.

● Team blazer with trousers and cable knit sweater for casual wear.

● A cherry-red silk shirt with matching skirt and black jacket.

● The black suit with a cream collarless blouse.

A basic wardrobe using red, white and blue – with an accent of green – is infinitely flexible. Here are some of the key pieces around which a basic wardrobe works. Start quite small, and build it up gradually buying quality garments in toning and contrasting colours.

- The black trousers with long cardigan and matching sweater.
- The black dress on its own or with a belted cardigan.
- White trousers with white cable-knit sweater.
- White trousers with black silk shirt and black blazer.
- Black polo neck, white trousers.
- Window shop at the best stores and buy the looks they show in shops at your price range.

Once you have the basics, you may decide to add extras to your wardrobe for more variety and to take you through the seasons. Good options are a houndstooth skirt or trousers, a geometric print black and white shirt with splashes of colour, an irresistible kitten-soft pastel angora sweater, a soft wool cream or pink jacket. A bold pattern check (plaid) shirt or jacket for a more casual look is a nice change from the staid jacket.

Variations The basic black dress lends itself to different looks. Take these ideas, for example:
- add a short white cropped jacket, with black patent acessories, to give a crisp, sophisticated look;
- a geometric print cardigan or tunic, in blue and black, white and black, or yellow and black will add pizazz and colour;
- a large shawl with bright colours on a dark background, pinned to your shoulder, worn loose or belted, is another option.

Jewellery achieve different looks with tailored, large or glitzy jewellery in silver or gold. Don't be timid! Jewellery adds impact – use it to make a statement.

Your colours
For blacks, black, royal blue and cream
For Orientals, plum, pink and red
For brunettes, black, red and white. For a less dramatic look, try a combination of navy, burgundy and taupe.
For blondes, cocoa, sand and pink
For redhead, camel, cream and pimento-red
For grey hair, denim blue, rose pink and cream

The nucleus of a good working wardrobe is the matching suit. The blazer jacket can be worn for sporty or formal occasions with or without a belt.

Left The Chanel tweed-striped cardigan makes a chic, sophisticated alternative to the blazer jacket. With pearls and gold chains it can easily carry through from day to evening.
Below left An ideal, classic combination for warm weather occasions – smart enough for a business meeting, casual enough for lunch with a friend.
Below right The cotton-knit, patterned sweater makes a bold statement for casual wear and adds zing to plain navy trousers.
Opposite The blazer jacket projects a smart but feminine feel, here, teamed with a silk shirt and flowing polka dot skirt.

Style

ACCESSORIES AND HOW TO WEAR THEM

Accessories are fashion's magic props. They change the character of an outfit, create a quality look, add style, and transform the ordinary into the 'extraordinary'. Accessories make dressing fun! Use them to create a dramatic, casual or sophisticated mood and to express your individuality. Use accessories for those finishing touches that pull together an outfit and update and upgrade a wardrobe. Accessories are the extras that give your wardrobe more mileage by transforming the same outfit from casual to classic, from day to evening, from season to season.

Be bold and keep up with the changes. Just as colours and shapes change with the seasons, so too do accessories. The wrong style shoe for a particular outfit will spoil the 'look'. If this year's look is strong and bold, give pretty but discreet jewellery a rest.

Use accessories to create a mood or to highlight your best feature. Create your own fashion signature with an oversized pair of zany red-framed glasses which not only accentuate your flaming red hair but also create an up-beat mood.

> THE SMALLEST ITEM CAN MAKE THE MOST POWERFUL STATEMENT. ACCESSORIES ARE BOLD PUNCTUATION MARKS WHICH GIVE THIS YEAR'S LOOK TO LAST YEAR'S CLOTHES.
>
> Liz E London

● If your budget precludes your buying the best in everything, try to invest in a few quality acessories that add prestige to your wardrobe: a fine leather handbag, beautiful shoes, the best watch you can afford.

● If you can't afford the real thing, get a good copy. If you can't afford a quality outfit invest in one great scarf or a magnificent paisley or print shawl.

● If you're going to invest in one major accessory, make it a purse or a briefcase if you are a professional; a great blazer if you are a suburban homemaker.

● The main rule of accessories is: when in doubt, don't! Too much clutter cheapens an outfit. And again, no matter how expensive the accessory, if it is the wrong proportion, if it overpowers you, *you* won't look good.

SHOES

The key to a basic shoe wardrobe is to keep it simple, classic and comfortable. The style of shoe can contribute or detract from the mood and balance of an outfit. Casual or thick soled shoes look wrong with a dressy outfit; high-heeled open, strappy shoes look wrong with sporty clothes. Flat shoes can be worn for day or evening, depending on the style and texture of the shoe. A flat pump can be classic and can work for both day and evening whereas a thick-soled flat shoe only works with comfortable casual and sporty clothes. The mid-heel pump can be both dressy or casual while the highest heel is usually for evening and must be worn with caution, especially by the shorter woman, since it can throw your body off balance and alter the gait of your walk.

A basic shoe wardrobe should consist of seven pairs of shoes: one walking shoe or sneaker; one flat shoe; three pairs of pumps (one in a slingback style for evening or summer); one evening shoe; and one pair of boots.

Fabrics leather, suede, crocodile or lizard are the most luxurious. In summer, espadrilles or fabric shoes.

Colours neutrals are the most practical – black, brown, taupe, tan or navy. For extra impact add burgundy, forest green, plum or red.

Dare to be different! Try something new! A subtle motif that coordinates with your shoe or a colour that contrasts creates originality and style to an otherwise ordinary outfit.

PANTYHOSE

If you are not sure of the right shade to wear for an outfit, it is safer to match hose to shoes than to match hose to skirt or dress. The general rule is wear tone on tone — that is, the same shade of shoe and hose.

Different textures create different effects. Fancy styles with dots or mesh are both feminine and flirtatious. Neutral sheers are best worn with pumps for business. An alternative is sheer nearly-black hose worn with black pumps.

A luxurious way to fill any v-neck collar. Open the scarf to full square or rectangle. Tie a knot in the centre by gathering the fabric. Reverse and tie at the back with the fullness placed at the 'v' of the collar. (Make sure knot is tied on the reverse side of the fabric.)

If you wish to draw attention to your legs, consider shiny or shimmering pantyhose or details like a bow or motif at the ankle or heel. This can be both eye-catching and dramatic. Dare to try interesting combinations of bright colours with dark shoes, or rich renaissance colours — mulberry, loganberry, amethyst, forest green or burgundy — with matching suede shoes.

SCARVES

Never underestimate the power and versatility of a good scarf. You can use it as a turban, a bandana, a collar, a bow or a sash, to pull together an outfit or give a new look to an old dress. Use it as a colour accent. A brilliant scarf on a plain outfit transforms it into sheer elegance.

The best of scarves are in black and white, in graphics, dots, stripes and checks as they add design to a plain dark outfit. Silk is perfect for a scarf because it looks and feels good and holds its shape better than one made of polyester. A must for every classic dresser is a colourful Hermès-type equestrian or nautical pattern, which will add an interesting quality look to a tailored outfit. Fasten with a wonderful stick-pin or cameo to transform the ordinary into the 'extra'ordinary'.

Special note

● A hint of a scarf showing around the neck can replace jewellery.

● Tie a small scarf to your handbag strap for a dash of colour.

● Distinctive oblong scarves in rich classic patterns, like foulards, paisley, stripes and dots can be found at better men's stores.

JEWELLERY

There is no substitute for real jewellery. If you can afford it, go for the best. If you can't, fake it — but make sure it's in good taste. When in doubt, go for classic shapes in real-looking gold or gems.

The classic piece of jewellery is still a good string of pearls. Pearls add a touch of class to a simple wool dress and are a perfect foil for chains or mixed with

Use a scarf to add colour and design to a plain outfit. Create a dramatic air by folding the scarf in a triangle and tying the corner in a knot or by creating the effect of a knot by gathering with a rubber band. Wear it with flair over one shoulder.

another stone, like haematite. The most flattering and versatile length for most women is the 24–26 inch length – which can be worn long or doubled as a choker.

Special note
- A watch is a status symbol – go for the best you can afford or for a great fake.
- Make a statement with one or two long chain necklaces. They are marvellous for suits.
- A neat chain bracelet, worn with a watch, adds a subtle touch.
- Classic earrings: hoop style, geometric style, coins, or button clip-ons are wonderful staples.
- For a more dramatic look, choose large silver geometric shapes or dazzling dangles.
- If you wear glasses, wear smaller earrings.
- For a high-power executive look, wear a silver cuff bracelet or a large, simple silver or gold brooch.
- Large coin earrings or Chanel-style large pearl earrings on a gold setting are great for a rich look.
- Don't wear too many pieces of matching jewellery.

BELTS
The classic wardrobe includes two or three leather or skin belts. Choose one that best suits your figure.
For the short-waisted, a very narrow belt or one that dips in the front. For example, a 3 chain or peplin style.
For the heavier woman, a long tie-style or a narrow belt with an interesting serpent or chain fastening.
For the long-waisted, a wider belt.
For the average woman, a contour shape or classic width and trim is best.
Black is the most practical choice, but consider browns and greens to accent both black and brown clothing. To add a distinctive look to a plain knit outfit, skirt or suit, indulge in a distinctive embossed leather belt. A safe width is 1½–2 inches. An alligator, snake, or soft suede belt can alter the mood of the plainest outfit. Rows of chains that drop below the waist are a wonderful accessory and give a Chanel look to a suit.

HANDBAGS AND ATTACHÉ BAGS

The surest way to upgrade your wardrobe is through the acquisition of an expensive, good quality handbag. Your handbag and shoe colours should compliment each other but need not match. Your shoes should be darker in tone than your handbag. You can spend a lot of money on a quality handbag and spoil it by overfilling. Make sure the style you choose can hold the items you need without looking overstuffed.

Think proportion when choosing your handbag. Take into consideration your overall shape and height. A very wide handbag makes a heavy woman look larger; an oversize pouch bag makes the short woman look smaller. If you are very tall, you can carry off an exceptionally large tote bag. Models use these because they are so practical — they hold just about everything. The smaller version of the tote bag is very sporty and good for casual wear.

Handbags come in four basic shapes: the clutch or envelope; the tote; the satchel; and the barrel. Using these, designers have come up with a bag for every occasion. Here are some of them:

The weekender, a casual, sporty shoulder strap bag. It can be in vinyl with leather trim or canvas, in pouch, barrel, or envelope shape. It can have a motif (like Louis Vuitton) or be plain with contrasting piping. It must be large enough to hold cosmetics and travel documents.

The workbag, a classic tailored medium-sized bag to wear with suits and dressier clothing. Your best choice would be a black calfskin shoulder strap in an envelope shape. The classic Chanel style quilted bag, with gold chain strap, is a chic alternative that can go from day into evening. It has an expensive look and doesn't date.

The additional bag, a lush hunter-green works well with most colours. Suede is an alternative to the leather bag but requires more care and does not wear as well. For summer you can wear the same style but in cream colour. Your summer bag can be woven or in a leather lattice design.

The evening bag, a clutch style in silk, satin, velvet or leather. For very dressy occasions, a jet beaded bag or mother of pearl. Classic shapes don't date as quickly as the more unusual shapes.

The Attaché case If you are a professional choose the finest quality you can afford. It is your status symbol and a very professional touch. Keep in mind proportion. A narrow one always looks neater. An attaché case looks smarter without a handbag.

HAT

Hats can add an elegant, dramatic or whimsical look to an outfit. The turban, the wide brimmed Spanish style or the coquettish wispy evening cocktail hat add colour and polish to an outfit and add an aura of excitement and drama. The large brim hat, coquettishly tilted to one side, adds mystery. The Princess of Wales is a great example of someone who uses hats to turn heads.

Special note

- An upturned brim is youthful and most flattering to the profile; a down brim exaggerates a large nose.
- A very tiny hat tends to look silly on a very large woman.
- A tall shape, like a Cossack style, adds inches to the short woman

GLASSES

The days of men never making passes at girls who wear glasses are over. Latch onto the latest in essential accessories now!

Sunglasses

You can create a sensational fashion image and an aura of instant celebrity by wearing flattering sunglasses. They make a marvellous fashion accessory. From the smörgåsbord of choices, choose sun specs that provide optimum protection for your eyes in a style that flatters the shape of your face. Wear them to:

- camouflage circles under the eyes or detract from a squint
- add instant colour to perk up your face
- add an air of mystery to complete a look

For breakfast at Tiffany's or the Ladies Annual Luncheon, make your entrance in this great dusty rose hat and contrasting check jacket. Add statement-making jewellery, the real thing if you can afford it, or fake it with great stone-studded copies.

Glasses

Choose a frame that is in proportion to your face: for a round face, small glasses; for wide-set eyes, choose a larger frame; for close-set eyes, a smaller frame. As a general rule, the three features to take into account are: the colour of your hair, the shape of your face; and the height of your eyebrows. Tinted lenses are sophisticated and flattering to the face; they can also help camouflage thick lenses.

Special note

● Rose and peach tones make lines around the eyes fade or disappear.

● Glasses are now available with a moveable lens, so you can lift each lens individually when applying make-up to your eyelids.

Dark, tinted lenses draw attention to the eye area, including circles under the eyes. If this is a problem, apply concealer under the eyes. Brown lenses can make you look tired. Blue lenses tend to make eye make-up colour disappear. Pink lenses add colour to your cheeks.

Old glasses can date you almost as much as an old fashioned hair-style, so keep up with the new shapes. Shop around for frames, prices vary enormously from store to store.

WHAT IS STYLE?

Be original! Style is the individual way that you package yourself; it reflects your experience and sense of fun. Try using colour as a dramatic fashion statement: black and white, camel and cream. Invent original ways to combine the rings on your fingers to co-ordinate your bracelets and bangles and for using scarfs and belts.

● wear earrings as clips on jacket ● wear several rings on your little finger ● combine a chain bracelet with your metal band watch ● wear a chain bracelet on the shoulder as an epaulette ● tie 2 long scarves together mingling pattern and colour ● wear a large shawl as a blouson over a dress.

Style is . . . the way you wear it. Combine contrasting textures, experiment with ways to wear jewellery, add a flattering hat and walk out in style!

Looks

CREATING AN ILLUSION

No-one is born with a perfect figure or a wardrobe full of clothes which gives them that million-dollar look every time. Even models and actresses, who appear to look terrific effortlessly, are well-schooled in the many tricks and techniques which create an illusion of perfection. We'd like to share these with you. If they can look ten pounds thinner and ten years younger through their choice of clothes and accessories – so can you!

Did you know that . . .

- a V-neck blouse can add length to a short neck and detract from a heavy bosom
- a long chain can make you look taller
- a drop chain belt makes you look longer waisted and slimmer
- a heavy woman can wear bright colours and look slimmer

> **T**HINGS AREN'T ALWAYS WHAT THEY SEEM?
> SKIM MILK MASQUERADES AS CREAM . . .
>
> William S. Sullivan

Here are guidelines to help you choose flattering clothes which leave you looking slim and beautiful.

Looking slimmer
Smooth fabrics such as gaberdine, flat-texture matt

jerseys, flannel or flat knits take pounds off your figure. The wrong choice adds pounds and width; clingy fabrics emphasize bulges; nubby fabrics and heavy tweeds can thicken and shorten the body. Pattern must be in proportion to body shape. Large bold patterns or plaids, or tiny delicate motifs are in the wrong proportion for the heavy figure.

The most common figure problems for women are heavy thighs and big hips. You can disguise this with skirts that hug the top of the hips with the fullness falling gently at the thigh. Avoid dresses and skirts with gathers at the waist and trousers with excess pleats. The best choice in a jacket is one that falls on the waist; one that ends at the largest part of your hips draws attention to this area.

One way to make a not-so-slim waist appear slimmer is to draw the eye away from the waist by choosing a belt that fastens on the hip. Avoid wide belts, they draw attention to the waist. You can also camouflage a wide waist with a blouson-style blouse or dress or a colourful waistcoat (vest) that falls beneath the waist line.

If you are heavy and rather short, choose styles that camouflage this look. To give the illusion of a long, lean, line use a monochromatic colour scheme wearing shades of the same colour from head to toe. Balance is very important in maintaining a chic look. Choose jackets that are cropped at the waist or tunic length for a more flattering line. A two-and-a-half-inch heel is the most flattering. Avoid stiletto heels – they may make you feel taller but the effect is down-market. A small head will make you appear taller. Avoid bouffant hair styles as a large head looks out of proportion to a small body.

Avoid • heavy quilted fabrics • long-haired furs • wide belts • heavy textured hose • large prints • bulky high socks and socks with cuffs, • thick soled or strappy, delicate shoes if you have thick ankles

Choose • well-proportioned jacket and skirt • tunic-length sweaters and jackets (make sure the skirt length is in proportion – not too long) • an outfit in different tones of the same colour • hose to match shoes and hemline • boots to co-ordinate with long skirts.

Break the rules occasionally. Although turtlenecks are not recommended for the short-heavy person, you can adapt one to suit your shape: if your neck is short, wear a mock-turtle neck that does not fold over; if your neck is long, your turtleneck can be slightly fuller. Look slim while you exercise: for golf, culottes, not too full and just above the knees; for tennis, wear peds or half-socks with pom-poms; for swimming, one piece bathing suit, sarong style, or one with a little skirt provided it is not bulky; avoid large prints and horizontal lines.

Status symbols
• Shoes from Gucci, Chanel • handbags from Louis Vuitton, Hermès or Fendi • jewellery from Cartier, Chanel, Bulgari • watches from Dunhill, Cartier, Rolex • clothes from Yves St Laurent, Chanel, Valentino, Céline • sun glasses: Porche, Rayban, Oliver Goldsmith

PERFECT PROPORTIONS
Nobody has perfect proportions, but that need not prevent you from looking like you do! Here's how you can make the most of the body you were born with:

If you have a large bust . . .
A sure sign of the mature woman is a drooping bust. While a well-fitting, comfortable bra is very important, a lift is a must. Select wide shoulder straps for extra support; elastic straps are more comfortable.
Avoid • clothes that are restricting or constraining
Choose • belts on the hip • vests/waistcoats •unfitted jackets • blouson style shirts and dresses

If you have a short waist . . .
Avoid • turtle necks • wide belts • short fitted jackets • empire style clothes • a dark belt on a white outfit • a deep raglan style
Choose • a V-neck coat style dress for a flattering vertical line • a V-neck rather than closed neck in sweaters, blouses and cardigans • longer length jackets • jackets with long lapels • long rope necklaces • a narrow belt the same colour as your blouse.

Left Wide, horizontal stripes are not a good choice for the shorter woman. They exaggerate the shortness and tend to make any woman look heavy busted – a feature to be particularly avoided without height on your side.

If you're short . . .

Although tall men feel protective towards the petite woman, steer clear of peter pan collars, puffed sleeves and flounces to maintain some authority. Keep your look neat, tailored and in proportion. Plain, lightly textured fabrics and patterns with a small motif will make you appear taller.

Choose • chanel style or single breasted jackets • shoulder pads • short cropped jackets • less bulky fabrics • hose to match shoes and outfit • vertical patterns and motifs

Avoid • raglan sleeves • very wide belts • empire style • very full sleeves or jackets • anything too young-looking • wide horizontal stripes.

Opposite A matching shirt and sweater with a vertical motif is a good choice for the curvy, shorter woman. Avoid wide belts and keep the look in tones of the same colour.

If you're tall . . .

Taller women look good in a layered look and can carry off large coats and wide or pleated trousers (pants). The art is to divide the body into equal proportions, so wear an eye-catching belt or try a skirt length just below the knee to 'cut' the leg.

<u>Choose</u> • full sleeves • tucks in skirt or trousers (pants) • light-coloured tights (panty hose) • sleeves with cuffs • large, bold patterns

<u>Avoid</u> • tiny prints • understated jewellery • three-quarter length sleeves • monochromatic outfits • vertical patterns and motifs • vertical stipes • skimpy high-waisted t-shirts

Opposite If you're tall you can afford to wear pleated trousers and waistcoat – it looks better with an accent of colour in the jacket to break up the uniformity of tone.

Left Long legs are most attractive but it's important to keep them in proportion. Here, the effect is of a short waist and long, long legs – the clothes exaggerate rather than flatter the figure.

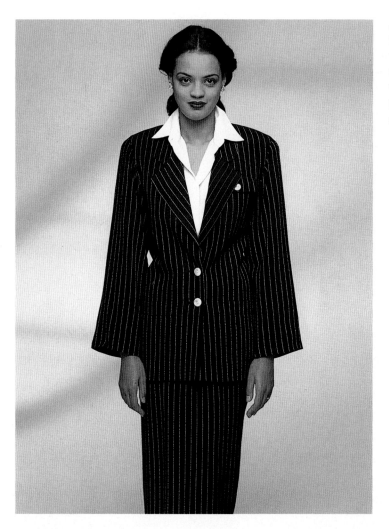

Left Vertical stripes serve only to exaggerate the pencil thin figure. This chic suit is unsuitable for the figure of this woman and actually detracts from an otherwise attractive appearance.

Left Vertical stripes serve only to exaggerate the pencil thin figure. This chic suit is unsuitable for the figure of this woman and actually detracts from an otherwise attractive appearance.

If you're very thin . . .

You will look marvellous in the layered look and can wear checks, plaids or patterns in a medium-sized print but there are features you may wish to de-emphasize, such as thin arms or neck.

Avoid ● sheer fabrics ● puffed sleeves ● sleeveless dresses ● clingy jersey ● fitted clothes

Choose ● high polo-necks ● triangular scarves tucked into V-neck shirts ● long-sleeved shirts ● ¾-length sleeves with chunky bracelets ● softly cut styles ● for golf, full culottes ● for tennis, a dress with very little flare at the bottom ● a swimsuit with a man's boxer-bottom style ● a leotard under a t-shirt with bermuda shorts.

Opposite Make the most of your height, because you're lucky to have it! You can afford to wear the whitest of outfits, the bulkiest of cable knits and as many layers as you like to add fullness to your figure.

If you're heavy . . .

The colour, texture and pattern of your clothes are important considerations to achieve a slimmer look.

Avoid ● clinging fabrics ● large checks (plaids) ● horizontal stripes ● skirts with bulk on hips ● patch pockets ● shoes with ankle straps ● boned girdle.

Choose ● vertical stripes ● neat patterns ● darker colours for heavy areas (if you're top heavy, wear a darker top).

Tip Don't be afraid of colour. If you love bright colours, wear a brightly coloured cardigan or long jacket over a dark outfit.

Opposite A flattering v-neck Chanel-style purple cardigan with a black border helps to define a vertical line which makes the torso look slender. A matching wool wrap finishes this smart outfit which sheds unwanted pounds in an instant.

Left Checks and plaids are unflattering to the heavy figure as they emphasize the breadth of the torso. Thick polo necks unfortunately bring attention to weight around the neck and face. The double-breasted cut of the jacket further adds to the feeling of bulk.

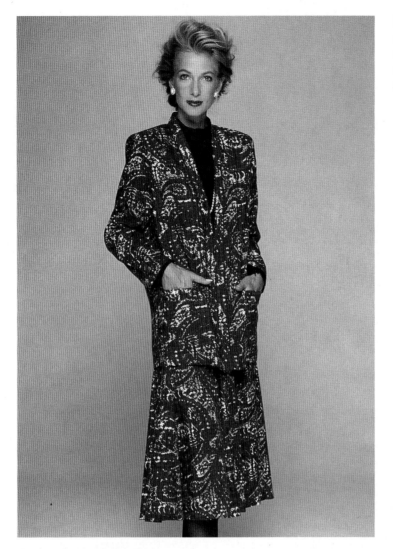

For a younger look . . .

You can project a younger image by wearing co-ordinated separates (jacket and skirt in different colour) rather than a matched suit. For a more vivacious look, wear bright colours. A jacket in a stiff fabric projects an older and more formal look. An unstructured jacket gives a youthful look when worn casually, with the sleeves rolled up.

<u>Avoid</u> ● stiff, structured fabrics ● dark colours ● hard handbags ● matching jacket and skirt/trousers ● dated make-up ● dated hairstyle ● dated glasses ● lipstick that runs into crease lines

<u>Choose</u> ● unstructured jackets ● bright colours ● tied bow on neckline ● co-ordinating (not matching) jacket and skirt/trousers ● jogging suit and sneakers ● the new season's shoes and accessories

For a quality look . . .

A neglected appearance and too-tight clothing are sure signs of a down-market image. Loose threads, cheap synthetic fabrics, unfinished hems and run-down shoes all contribute to a cheap-looking appearance. If you can't afford designer clothes but you want a quality look, you must know what to look for to make your clothes appear more expensive.

<u>Avoid</u> ● non leather shoes, other than canvas ● cheap, synthetic fabrics in faded colours ● trouser length too short or too long ● underpants 'line' showing through trousers ● a patterned outfit badly sewn so that the pattern does not match ● cheap synthetic sweaters ● ungroomed hairstyle ● sloppy appearance ● unheeled shoes

<u>Choose</u> ● a narrow reptile belt ● designer scarf ● long chain and pearl necklace ● quality fabrics

Opposite A casual outfit in a luxurious combination of texture and fabrics – the unmistakeable sign of quality dressing.

Left A combination of the bad choice of neckline – which does not enhance the neck area – and cheaply finished trousers with elasticated waist creates a poor quality look which should be avoided at all cost.

Left The dark paisley skirt teamed with a similarly dark top does little to show off the imagination and flair that this skirt offers.

Turn 'ordinary' into 'extra'ordinary' . . .

Why project an ordinary look when, with a little know-how, you can transform it into an extraordinary look? A simple black dress worn with a nice gold chain and earrings looks right, but ordinary. For a dramatic effect, take a black cape lined in emerald satin and throw it over one shoulder; fasten it with a cascading medieval brooch studded with red and green stones, wear drop jewel-toned earrings and complete the look with a crimson red lipstick. Alternatively, wear the simple black dress with sheer barely-black hose; black shoes with silver capped toes and heels; a black satin belt; and a diamanté drop pendant brooch clasped on the shoulder; finish with diamanté earrings.

Opposite Mix two paisley patterns, one light and one dark. Add a sophisticated accent and a marvellous black throw for drama. Fasten with a gold and stone brooch to transform the ordinary dull paisley into something extraordinary.

ingerie

LOOKING GOOD UNDERNEATH

The secret of a smooth, svelte line in clothing starts with choosing the right foundation. If you've worked hard to achieve a good figure don't spoil it by wearing the wrong underwear. Create the illusion of an even better figure by choosing undergarments that camouflage body flaws and make your clothes look better. Wearing the wrong foundation garments can ruin your look and make you look saggy, old, sloppy.

BRAS

Are you wearing the same style bra you wore ten years ago? If you haven't been measured for a bra recently, make sure you get yourself properly fitted. The best choice for every day wear is a 'natural' look. For cleavage or a decolléte dress, a slightly pushed up look may be desirable.

> SILK UNDERWEAR IS ONE OF LIFE'S PLEASURES. UNLIKE MOST OTHER TREATS IT IS NEITHER FATTENING, IMMORAL, NOR BAD FOR THE HEALTH
>
> Janet Reger

Have you been to a good lingerie shop recently? If not, you will be delighted by the variety of fabrics and styles including: seamed or seamless; plain or lace trimmed; no wire or underwire; sporty or cocktail; solid colour or patterned; padded, semi-padded or contoured bras for the small busted; excellent 'minimizer' or boned

bras for the fuller figure. When trying on a bra, bend, stretch and twist to check that it fits comfortably when you move.

Special occasion bras

- The seamless bra, usually a thin stretch or knitted fabric, creates the look of 'no-bra'. It looks great under smooth blouses. A variation of this is the sweater bra. This too has no wrinkles or seams, but comes in moulded and padded styles.
- The T-back, front-closure bra gives extra support and is usually worn for sports. It's a boon for those who hate reaching behind to fasten hooks.
- The strapless bra is designed to support the bust without straps and usually incorporates a push-up feature. It is also available in a natural sheer bandeau or tube, which creates a smoother line. When trying on a strapless make sure that you feel secure in it and that it stays up properly.
- The plunging bra is cut very low in the centre, often front fastening, and is ideal for decollété necklines.
- The halter bra has criss-cross straps that are detachable and can be worn as many as five different ways. Ideal for halter necks and backless dresses. A variation of this fastens at the waist for a backless dress.
- The cocktail stick-ons, for the small to average bust, are push-up moulds that cover half or the whole bust. These are for backless and sideless dresses.

PANTIES

Match at least three pairs of panties for every bra you own. You may want to vary the style of the panty – the bikini, the below-belly-button, the high brief. When trying on panties check that they do not ride up and that they are not too tight.

How to avoid panty lines:

- Waist briefs eliminate the bikini line
- Stretch-lace trim is preferable to elastic as it creates a smoother line at the leg
- French-cut thighs minimize visible panty lines

● G-briefs look good under clingy or stretch fabrics.

The controlled panty brief

If the stomach, hip and thigh are your problem areas, look slimmer in the new control foundations that are both lightweight and firming. There is a great range of styles to choose from; including a wide bandeau waist cincher, a panel control for the stomach or thigh area, and a high cut or long line leg style. Five per cent spandex (for control) will help a garment keep its shape; ten to twenty per cent will provide a light support; thirty per cent is considered a girdle.

For the small or average figure

A minimally elasticized panty in bikini or brief style is the best choice. An alternative is panty hose with a control top. For shorts or slacks, the bare minimal jock style bikini gives a natural look. This only works if you are firm. If you're not, select a style with a high cut thigh that does not cut into your leg. Another alternative is a regular brief that covers the complete waist to thigh area.

Tip Bikini briefs, cami knickers, the teddy or garters with suspenders are the sexiest.

For the heavy figure

The panty girdle, a more controlled garment, is the best choice. It has improved dramatically with new lightweight control panels in either the back, side, front or all three. An alternative to this is the one piece body type style which gives a smooth line from shoulder to hip.

COLOUR

The three basic colours in underwear are white, beige and black — safe, but not exciting. Jewel tones, bold prints, jungle flower and animal patterns liven up a dull underwear wardrobe. Be a little daring — treat yourself to something that makes *you* feel *special*!!

NIGHT TIME BEAUTY

Lingerie is a lovely way to treat yourself to something special. Get something that makes you feel absolutely beautiful and is just right for *you*. Fabrics plays an important part in the effect you want to achieve or the mood you want to project.

For warmth, go for flannel, cashmere or velveteen; for tropical climates, opt for 100% cotton.

FOR LOVELY LEGS

Dots, bows, butterflies, flowers — almost anything goes on tights and stockings these days. Explore different textures remembering that the more opaque and heavy the hose, the more casual the look. Colourful cotton lycras are amazingly versatile and can be quite dramatic in exciting colours like forest green, aubergine and off-white. But for a sexy evening look, choose sheer shimmery textures in colours that tone with your clothes and show off your chic shoes.

STYLES

A flowing V-neck caftan in a beautiful print and flattering colour is a good choice if you are heavy, large busted, tall or have large hips. Nice details to look for are embroidery or lace on sleeves or shoulders, or kimono-style sleeves.

Show off your good features, camouflage the less than perfect ones. If you have a good back or want to show off a fabulous tan, display it with a magnificent low back draped cowl neckline — *très chic*! If you have great legs, opt for the teddy style or a shirt style wrap. If you want to draw attention to your face or distract from large hips, choose a sailor-style, attention-seeking collar or some other interesting neckline.

If you've got great legs, flaunt them! Choose tights that have a slight shine. Or, you can draw attention to your legs with seamed stockings or motifs on the ankle. When they whistle it will be for you, not your dog!

Your colours

Dark skinned brunettes . . . white, red, pale pink, black, purple

Pale skinned brunettes . . . pale green, pale pink, off-white, ice-blue, navy, cherry-red

Blondes with pale skin . . . cream, ice-pink, hot pink, mauve, pale blue, cocoa

Blondes with tanned skin or high colouring . . . cream, camel, yellow, coral, lime, yellow, green, black, aqua

Redheads . . . cream, olive, pimento-red, camel, salmon, aqua

Orientals . . . ice-pink, turquoise, mauve, hot pink

Blacks . . . white, black, red, pale yellow, pale lime, hot pink, periwinkle blue

Grace

ELEGANCE · POISE · CARRIAGE

Did you ever notice a ballerina bending over to lace her ballet shoes, or a model confidently striding down a runway, pirouetting gracefully, her skirt swinging, and you say to yourself, 'Wow, if only I could look like that.' You may not have defined it, but likely as not you were admiring her gracefulness and posture.

A woman who has poise and grace conveys that very rare ingredient – 'presence' ... and a woman with presence conveys mystique ... confidence ... allure ... This special woman has mastered the art of 'perfect posture'. It is reflected in the way she stands, the way she sits, the way she moves, and even the way she holds her head.

SOME ARE BORN WITH IT, SOME HAVE IT NATURALLY, BUT MOST OF US HAVE TO PRETEND WE ARE HOLDING A COIN BETWEEN OUR SHOULDER BLADES.

Lucy Clayton, Charm School

POSTURE IS A WAY OF LIFE

Good posture can make you look ten pounds lighter; bad posture can make you look ten years older, *and feel it*. Your attitude toward life is reflected in your posture. Actresses who have stage presence have it; women who feel beautiful have it. You can have it too if you're willing to take the time to practise, and keep practising a few basic steps (see pages 112–113).

Poor posture can lead to physical ailments: disc and back problems, round shoulders, sway back, fatigue, headaches, stress. Years of poor posture can cause slumped shoulders, a protruding stomach and sagging breasts. If you have poor posture, no matter what your actual age, you will look older.

Stand tall! This does not mean a military front thrust but an erect carriage, keeping your head straight. Standing tall helps eliminate a double chin and a spare tyre; it makes a flabby middle look flat, whittles a waistline, lifts your bust and raises your spirits. And as a nice fringe benefit, it can make you look up to two inches taller.

How can you tell if you have good posture? To check, stand with your back to the wall and try to get your shoulders, buttocks and heels to touch the wall. Try to slide a hand behind the curve of your back. If it fits snugly, congratulations, your posture is good. If there is too much room it means the curve is too pronounced and you need to work on yourself. You are not alone. There isn't a woman with a sense of 'presence' who has not worked at it.

To practise good posture, stand tall with your shoul-

HOW YOU MOVE REVEALS HOW YOU FEEL

Lenna Ginis, movement instructor

Top left/right Whole back lengthener. Lie on your back with knees bent, feet apart and hands palm down at sides. Breathe in, raising both arms (*left*) and lifting hips off the floor until your arms are fully stretched out behind you (*right*).

Below left/right Low Back Stretch. Lie in the position shown (*left*). Inhale. Exhale as you bring your knees up to your chest and then inhale as you return to the start. Repeat 8–10 times.

ders back and down, head and neck held high, stomach in, knees relaxed. To hold your stomach in, tilt your pelvis forward slightly. An old Hollywood technique is to pretend you're a marionette with a string going up the back of your neck to the top of your head and pulling you upward. At first you may feel just like a puppet. But as your new posture becomes a part of you, it will feel more natural and above all, look and feel right.

How to stand

Stand with your weight placed evenly on both feet. Hold your head up and keep your back and shoulders straight. Hold your stomach in but not so much that you feel tense. Don't slouch forward, leaning on one foot, with your hands crossed in front of you, it looks 'old'.

How to sit

Sitting tall is just as important as standing tall. Sitting or standing, your spine should be in the same position — straight, not slouched. Sitting with your torso elongated makes you look long, lean and graceful. Sit with your spine against the chair back, your feet on the floor, your knees a little higher than your hips. Sit balanced on both buttocks so that your weight is evenly distributed. Keep your legs together. If you want to cross your legs, do it in an elegant way: ankles crossed, feet to a side, on an angle, the way actresses interviewed on TV often sit. Don't sit with your heels under the chair and your ankles crossed.

How to walk

Walk tall. Step forward lightly on the ball of your foot and land on your heel. If not, your gait will look stilted and you will create stress on your lower back. For walking, wear flat shoes or shoes with a one to two inch heel. High heels can pitch your body forward and put strain on your back. Models move gracefully not only because they walk tall but because they always walk from the hip rather than from the knee. It takes a bit of time to get used to a new way of walking but it's well worth it for the grace and confidence you will project. Don't lean for-

> **CHANGE THE IMAGE AND THE WALK WILL CHANGE**
>
> Hemitra Crecraft, dance therapist

To open caved-in rib cage, sit as shown. Press palms together for 5 seconds, then open, pushing together the shoulder blades.

ward as you walk; think like a model – walk from the hips.

How to pick up something
Bend at the knees and hips, keeping your back straight. If necessary, lean forward to reach the object, but return to an upright position <u>before</u> standing. Remember to bend at the knees. Don't stoop down from the waist, with your legs straight.

How to eat
Sit with your buttocks and back flat against the chair back. Try to sit in a chair that's low, so that your knees will be slightly higher than your hips. Sit close to the table. If you need to be closer to the food, lean forward from your hips.

Avoid slouching down over the plate to reach for the food. To help you remember, visualize dining with Paul Newman and imagine his admiring glance as you elegantly lean from the waist to reach for the caviar.

How to enter a room with poise
Think confident! Think tall! Think beautiful! No matter how you feel, act the part you wish to project. As you enter the room, take a deep breath to relax, and casually look around the room. Then move forward confidently as you smilingly greet your host or hostess.

Tip If you're with a man, avoid hanging on to his arm; instead, lightly rest your arm on his elbow as you walk in with your head held high and a gracious smile on your lips. This entrance is especially helpful for shy women.

How to get in and out of a car
To get in, put your hand on the door for balance, move as close as possible to the car seat, turn facing the door and seat yourself backward into the seat. For a smooth exit, move as close as possible to the door, step out with your outside foot, turn toward the outside door, with one hand on the door for balance, then gently raise yourself out. It may take a bit of practice, but it's worth it for the lovely, graceful effect.

Above A foot first plunge is an inelegant way of getting into a car. It stretches your clothes and makes you look ungainly.

Opposite With your back facing the seat of the car, lower yourself gracefully to sit on the edge of the seat. Then, with knees together, lift your legs gently into the car and adjust to reach a comfortable seated position.

Health

DIET · EXERCISE · RELAXATION

Mid-life is the beginning of the rest of your life. To slow down the process of ageing, you need to take responsibility for your physical and mental well-being. You need good nutrition, exercise, relaxation periods and 'mood changers'. Most of all you need to develop an attitude that is open to change and be determined to make this the best time of your life.

MENOPAUSE

Like all new beginnings there is some fear with the approach of menopause. Some women fear they will lose their looks, their sexuality, their femininity; but these myths have long been discredited. Most women pass through the menopause with very few problems. Some are less fortunate and suffer various problems including 'hot and cold flushes/flashes': feeling hot one moment, cold the next, and perspiring freely. A way to cope is to avoid 100% synthetics which make the skin feel clammy. Alternatively, your doctor might prescribe hormone replacement therapy (HRT) or evening primrose capsules.

AIM FOR EIGHT HOURS SLEEP, A HEALTHY, BALANCED DIET WITH FRESH FRUIT AND VEGETABLES, PLENTY OF WATER TO FLUSH OUT THE TOXINS AND A STRICT SKIN AND EXERCISE REGIME.

Molton Brown

NUTRITION

Eating is a pleasurable experience – make it a healthy one and it could make you live longer. The combination of staying fit with a regular exercise routine and selective eating of fresh fruit and leafy greens helps cure mental stress, keeps your body supple and reduces your chance of contracting some diseases.

Checklist

Your beauty problems could well be due to deficiences in your diet:

Do you have:	You may need:
Excess oiliness on your face	Vitamins B2 or B6
Dark circles around your eyes	Iron
Cracks on edges of lips	Vitamins B2 or B6
Fatty tumours on eyelids	Less cholesterol
Splitting nails	Calcium or protein
Thinning hair	Protein (or less Vitamin A)
Dry rough skin	Vitamins A or E
Acne	Less iodine

Dr Kanahara's Diet

A cleansing and weight loss diet, particularly good for urinary and bladder problems. It is a disciplined diet and one which achieves results over a period of 10–14 days.
Caution Check with your doctor before any diet.

Breakfast

Rice cakes (or 1 piece wholemeal bread); sesame margarine; tahini spread; carrot juice, bancha tea or dandelion coffee.

Lunch

Boil together the following mixture and flavour with soya sauce: millet, oats, shortgrain brown rice, kasha, aduki bean, any vegetables except cabbage, tomatoes, peppers, potatoes, corn. Eat with rice cakes (or 1 piece wholemeal bread). Carrot juice, bancha tea or dandelion coffee.

Healthy eating plan

EAT FOR ENERGY	**Complete carbohydrates:** potatoes brown rice grains pasta	millet legumes **Quick high (quick low):** sugar sweets	syrups soft drinks sweeteners fruit vegetables	moderate protein limited fat
EAT FOR HEALTH	brown rice wholemeal bread fibre (oatmeal, bran) chicken fish	fruit vegetables **Snacks:** raw vegetables carrot sticks	celery cauliflower raisins yoghurt	**Drinks:** herbal tea carrot, orange, apple juice postum skimmed milk
EAT FOR BRAIN POWER!	**Protein** cheese eggs lentils tofu fish fowl	**Mineral requirements** citrus fruits tomatoes sweet potatoes green leafy vegetables	**B vitamins in:** brown rice wholemeal bread meat peanuts bran	
ANTI-CARCINOGENIC	cantaloupe lots of fruit whole grains vegetables carrots broccoli	sweet potato winter squash	**Avoid** smoked foods animal fat high fat foods alcohol	
ANTI-AGEING	**Vitamin E rich foods** almonds walnuts peanut oil	wheatgerm milk eggs dark green vegetables		
ANTI-OSTEOPOROSIS	**Calcium-rich foods** milk cheese other dairy products	**Avoid** alcohol caffeine	CAUTION This is not a diet sheet. Instead it offers basic guidelines for healthy eating. Consult your doctor or dietician for a more detailed diet which caters for your particular needs.	

Dinner
Small piece of fish or meat; the above vegetable mixture or vegetables and brown rice.

General rules
Add to this basic diet but maintain the proportions 30% fish or chicken, to 70% vegetables.
Avoid sugar, salt, cakes, fruit (except apples), salad (except watercress). Drink plenty.

STRESS MANAGEMENT
We all have stress. It is part of life. In manageable doses, it can stimulate, challenge and motivate. However, too much stress needs to be defused before it becomes chronic. Here is a broad overview of some widely used stress techniques and stress defusers. Assess which one would best suit you and your lifestyle, then do some further research.

Autogenic training
Sit or lie down in a comfortable position and repeat a few simple, standard phrases, such as 'My hand feels warm and heavy' or 'My breathing is calm and regular'. Use it after a particularly difficult day, to relax your muscles and 'centre yourself'.

Biofeedback
Biofeedback assesses how the body reacts to stress. Apparatus is used to monitor brain waves, muscle tension and body temperature. Once the stress symptoms are diagnosed one is taught to cope with them by learning how to control such things as heart rate, blood pressure and skin temperature. The technique is used to treat problems such as hot flushes/flashes, menstrual cramps, insomnia and chronic muscle pain. This is for you if you like a sense of control over your body and have the time and money for the sessions.

Breathing
Abdominal breathing or yoga breathing is a good technique to learn. Most people breathe incorrectly and

when under stress their breathing becomes even more shallow. Abdominal breathing gets more oxygen into the body and is an effective way to cope with anxiety. It takes only a few minutes, and can be used during or before stressful situations – when you're caught in traffic, just before an important meeting or at the end of the month when you're opening the bills.

<u>Technique</u> Abdominal, or deep breathing involves learning how to breathe correctly. It takes a bit of practice, but is well worth it:

1 Inhale slowly and deeply through your nose; at the same time, slowly expand your stomach as far as you can. Place your hand lightly on your stomach to feel it inflate.

Be tempted by strawberries, grapes, apples and any other of your favourite fruits. Get into the habit of making every day a healthy fruit-filled day. Fruit is not only good for you but will also help keep off those extra pounds.

2 Exhale slowly and deeply through your nose; at the same time slowly pull in your stomach as far as you can.

(A good visualization technique to use during this exercise is to imagine that the abdomen is a balloon and you are slowly filling it with empty air, then slowly emptying it.)

Hatha yoga

Hatha Yoga is a system of exercises and breathing techniques that both relax and energize. When doing the slow stretching exercises, the emphasis is on breathing and concentration. The pace is slow and easy, can be done by young and old and is particularly good for those who dislike strenuous forms of exercise.

Progressive relaxation

To control muscle tension, one is taught to systematically tense and relax the muscles in the body. It's very easy and it works. One starts by tensing and relaxing one foot, then the other foot, then progressively goes to the upper parts of the body, ending with tensing and relaxing the face and head. If you have trouble falling asleep because of stress-related muscle tension, this is an excellent way to completely relax your entire body.

Trancendental meditation

To meditate, you sit in a comfortable position, in a quiet environment where you will not be disturbed. You take a word, or sound, and repeat it silently for 20 minutes, twice a day. The word or sound is the 'mantra', which is meant to divert attention from the thought processes and 'still' the mind. Few people can commit themselves to meditating twice daily for 20 minutes, but those who do claim it clears the mind, cures insomnia and strengthens the immune system.

Aromatherapy

During an Aromatherapy treatment, oils containing the pure essences of plants, herbs or flowers are gently massaged into the skin. The gentle, soothing strokes of the facial massage, the healing effects of the oil and the fragrant aromas soothe the mind and chase away cares.

Reflexology – (zone therapy)

Basically a foot massage, but it's more than just having your toes tickled. The theory is that certain pressure points on the feet correspond to certain parts of the body. When applying pressure to these parts, organ and gland functions benefit, toxins are released, circulation is improved and stress related problems are relieved. Apart from these benefits it is marvellously relaxing and makes you feel like dancing!

Coping

Some people can handle stress easily; others find it more difficult. How do you rate your coping style?

Treat yourself to a visit to a spa or health club where you can indulge in a soothing massage. It will help you relax, improve your circulation and bring down your stress level.

Do you . . .
- have confidence in yourself?
- share your problems with others?
- take steps to solve your problems?
- plan strategy and anticipate problems?

If you can answer 'yes' to all these your coping ability is high. Coping also means: having a network of friends and acquaintances; regularly attending clubs or social activities; having the ability to organize your time effectively; occasionally relaxing and doing something that is 'fun'; keeping positive about life.

Do you . . .
- feel helpless and believe you can't 'win'?
- procrastinate or worry about the problem?
- avoid discussing your problems and asking for help?
- fail to take action to change the situation?

If you answer 'yes' to all these, your coping ability is low and it might be time to seek professional help. Other tell-tale characteristics include: little sleep; alcohol or high caffeine consumption; an inability to 'play'.

Mood changers
- Meet a friend for lunch
- Listen to music
- Rent a comedy video
- Take a brisk 20 minute walk
- Treat yourself to something special . . .

When you need to get away from it all, and long for a bit of self-indulgence, check in at a spa. Spas range from simple retreats to the ultimate in luxurious pampering. Facilities include exercise classes, swimming, sauna, sunbed and tennis courts. Pampering can include a facial, mud pack, massage, pedicure, reflexology, acupuncture, aromatherapy or hydrotherapy (a mineral salt bath with high-pressure jets) and, of course, a diet geared for your needs. Whether it's for a three day or two week stay, you'll return home marvellously refreshed, deliciously relaxed, and a few pounds lighter.

Meet a friend for lunch and have a great laugh or a good gossip. It's a great way to spend an hour or two and a beneficial way of reducing your stress level.

WHY EXERCISE?

- To look younger
- To lose weight
- To firm up, trim up
- To have more energy
- To feel more calm, more self-confident
- To clear the mind and increase concentration

We all know we need to exercise to look better, feel better. Doctors emphasize the benefits to the body; psychologists recommend it because it releases stress and hostility and calms the mind; beauty experts recommend it for a healthy, glowing skin. Exercising regularly can turn the biological clock back 20 years but getting motivated is difficult. However, remember the benefits!

You are more likely to remain with an exercise program if you make it fun! Try something new — an exercise video, tap-dancing, jazz exercise. Make exercise an excuse to be with a friend. A sport like tennis can burn off excess energy and maintain social contacts. Swimming is a less strenuous alternative and is year round.

Walking is for all ages. It is an easy, enjoyable way to stay fit and lose weight. Not only does it tone your legs and body, it helps your body to consume more oxygen and makes you feel and sleep better. For a brisk walk, use long strides and swing your arms. For motivation, remember that a brisk walk one hour a day can lead to a weight loss of 8–12 lb a year (when practised in conjunction with a calorie-controlled diet).

Do warm up stretches before you begin any strenuous exercise and taper off slowly before you stop. It is sensible to check with your doctor before starting any exercise programme.

SEXUAL FITNESS

Any form of sustained exercise appears to work as an aphrodisiac. Women who exercise regularly gain more self-confidence and enjoy sex more. It is a myth that sexual desire and fitness decline with time. In fact, a woman's sexual drive and enjoyment of sex increases at menopause. Include a few pelvic exercises in your

Tennis is an exciting sport which will keep you fit and provide you with a social life — especially if you join a club.

Right Stretches: Stand on toes and reach for the ceiling stretching the spine; stretch to the left and right; stretch forward; and stretch towards the floor (bend knees slightly if difficult). Repeat until you feel limber.

Left Waist bends: place one hand on the waist and the other stretched towards the ceiling. Bend to the side five times. Change hands and repeat five times on the other side.

Right Mobility moves: place one hand on your waist and the other stretched out at shoulder height and rotate the wrist twenty times in each direction. Now rotate from the shoulder. Repeat with other arm.

Above left/centre Leg swings: holding onto a barre and standing straight with legs apart, swing one leg – with the knee straight – across and back the upright leg and raise. Change legs and repeat. Start with 15 and work up to 50.

Above right In the position shown, raise your leg forward and swing back. Change direction and repeat with right leg.

exercise program to maintain or increase your sexual flexibility. If sexual desire wanes, it could be due to medication you have been prescribed.

Safe sex involves learning to discover new erogenous zones. Safe sex gives you the chance to rediscover the pleasure of touch, body massage, caressing, hugging and cuddling. See your doctor if you are unsure about the best form of protection for you and your partner.

LATE PREGNANCY

More and more women are choosing to postpone motherhood until later in life. With advances in medical research and technology the likelihood of a troublefree pregnancy and birth are better than ever. Do everything to maintain your health and fitness at peak level.

● Make sure you are not deficient in vitamins or minerals. Mineral supplements may be necessary to help ensure a healthy and happy baby.

● Do yoga exercises designed for pregnant women, to keep you fit and make the birth process easier.

● Talk and sing to the baby when pregnant, play soothing music. Parents who talk and sing to the foetus produce babies who are more receptive to their parents' voices and to music.

● Alkaline and medicated soaps can aggravate skin problems brought on by pregnancy. Caffeine, too, can have a negative effect on 'pregnant skin'.

ATTITUDE

All the exercise, nutrition and relaxation techniques in the world will be wasted without a positive fun-loving attitude. Boredom and apathy can age you almost as fast as poor nutrition and lack of exercise. People who don't grow, stagnate; they lose interest in life; they grow old before their time. A youthful, positive attitude encourages growth and leads to the development of new interests, new horizons. New interests make you more interesting – to yourself and to others. Dare to be the best you can be! Grow, expand, break old habits, climb more mountains . . . And above all, enjoy life!

Travel

LUGGAGE · PREPARATIONS

Travel is a great way to widen your horizons, to meet new and interesting people. When you travel, your luggage, like your appearance, makes an impression on fellow travellers. It affects how you are perceived and how you are treated. Travel in style! Better luggage usually means faster and more solicitous service. Good quality, durable luggage also lasts a lifetime – make sure it is waterproof and that you can manage to carry it. There will always be times when it's impossible to get someone to carry it for you.

PREPARING TO TRAVEL
Making any sort of journey is always a stressful experience and also a time when, because there is so much going on, it's easy to forget the most important things. Make use of professionals as much as you can and keep a checklist!

Your travel agent
A travel agent can save you time, money and aggravation – and there is no charge for his services. Don't forget to ask about car hire, visas, insurance.

> **T**RAVEL, IN THE YOUNGER SORT, IS A PART OF EDUCATION; IN THE ELDER, A PART OF EXPERIENCE.
>
> Francis Bacon

Personal checklist

- Check that your passport is not out of date.
- Go over your medical insurance to see what coverage you have outside the country.
- Remember to pack your medication. Many over-the-counter drugs require a prescription in other countries.
- If you are travelling to developing countries, you may need immunization shots to protect you against certain diseases. Get these as early as possible, in case you have an adverse reaction.

PACKING

Leave yourself plenty of time to pack, and write and use a list. Remember some airlines charge a considerable fee for excess luggage, so check your allowance.

Hand luggage

Airlines allow one carry-on bag which has to fit under the seat or in the overhead compartment. A soft-sided bag is the most practical. In it pack your travellers cheques, credit cards, passport, tickets, hotel and car rental confirmations, driver's licence, foreign pocket dictionary, small valuables, an extra pair of glasses or contact lenses with solution, and perhaps a camera. Include basics you will need if your luggage gets lost: medication, a change of underwear, nightgown, toothbrush and toothpaste. If you have the room, pack an extra pair of hose, folding slippers and sweater. And don't forget a good book or magazine to read en route.

What to carry in your handbag

- keys, cash, address book, itinerary, pen and notebook
- cosmetic bag containing lipstick, comb, brush, nailfile, blusher, eye make-up, compact, tissues.
- chewing gum, sweets and candies to avoid ear-popping during take-off and landing.

Packing tips

- Roll soft items of clothing like sweaters, nightgowns, jeans, belts, for neater packing. Trousers can be folded or rolled. To roll them, put them on a flat surface, and roll up tightly from the bottom, pulling the seams out as you roll. To fold, insert tissue paper between the fold.

- Fold dresses and skirts along the seam lines.
- Place shoes and heavy items towards the back of the suitcase, opposite the handle.
- Pack fragile items as near to the middle as possible and tightly surround them with soft clothing.

Nice extras that you may like to include: a pocket calculator to translate currency: an immersion coil for making coffee or tea in your room; a portable cassette player with a few of your favourite tapes.

Your cosmetic bag

If you travel a lot, a permanently packed beauty bag is a great time-saver. The best choice of cosmetic bag for travel is a hanging multiple pocket plastic cosmetic bag that rolls into a pouch. The well-equipped cosmetic bag contains small plastic bottles or containers and is stocked with the following:

Cosmetics foundation, two shades of blush, two lipsticks, lipstick pencil, pencil sharpener, concealer, two eye-shadows, mascara, lipfix, eye-lash curler.

Skin products night-cream, eye-cream, cleanser, face

Save yourself trouble by having your cosmetic bag packed and ready to go. Make yourself a check list and tick off each item as it goes into the bag – it can be a nightmare trying to find your favourite shades abroad.

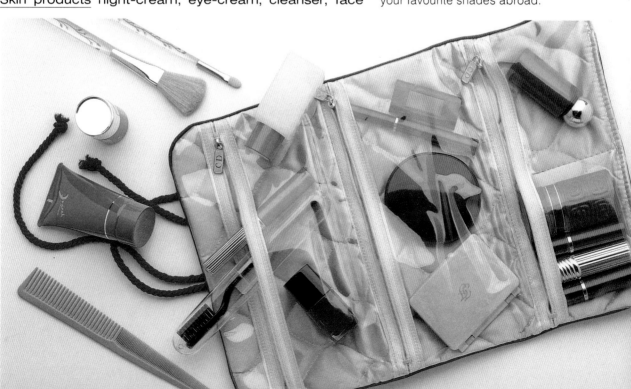

mask, moisturizer, eye-make-up removing pads, cotton balls, Q-tips, tweezers.

Body products toothbrush, toothpaste, dental floss, nail polish, nail polish remover pads, nail file, deodorant, razor or hair removal cream, body lotion, bath oils, tanning lotion, sunscreen.

Hair products brush, hair spray, hair mousse, shampoo, conditioner, dryer, hair rollers, hair clips, hair combs.

Optional Small sewing kit, electric adapter for international travel, packets of laundry soap, clothes steamer or travel iron, clothes pegs.

Packing for a one-week city trip

The key to efficient travelling is to pack the minimum number of clothes that mix and match so that you can change the look of your outfits. Build your wardrobe around a two or three colour combination. Navy, khaki and cream or black, white and taupe are two successful combinations. The following list will give you six changes of outfit that will fit into a suitcase small enough to carry on as cabin luggage.

- Travel in a suit; five tops; a skirt in a colour that co-ordinates with your suit skirt; one sweater; two belts; two pairs of shoes; jewellery.

Your six outfits

- A silk blouse and skirt – for day or evening, depending on jewellery.
- Polo neck top and trousers – for day.
- Skirt and belted sweater – for day.
- Print blouse with alternate skirt – for evening.
- Suit with camisole – for evening.
- Trousers and jacket with turtle neck – for day or casual evening wear.

Resort wear

For a poolside holiday, travel light. Bring comfortable, easy-care clothes that are versatile and make you look good day and night. Stick to two colours, so that all your separates are interchangeable. Be sure to include:

- four bathing suits – two for sunning and two for swimming;

- shorts, (tennis skirt optional) tee-shirts, cover-ups, sun dress;
- sandals, sneakers, flip-flops and soft, smart shoes for evening;
- at least one pair of cotton trousers, two skirts and blouses and an unconstructed jacket to travel in;
- two dresses;
- a few belts and some bright jewellery – possibly a fun, waterproof watch;
- a lightweight shawl, for cool summer nights and chilly air-conditioned rooms;
- cosmetics — include waterproof mascara and bright

For a sunshine cruise or sailing holiday, choose white or off-white. A cotton knit teamed with white, red or pastels looks right in sunny climates and is a great neutral to go with all your summer separates.

coloured lipsticks; the darker you tan, the brighter the lipstick; for evening, use a darker tone of foundation;
- sun visor, sunglasses, sunhat.

Special note
- Never use perfume in the sun – it can cause spots.
- If hair is coloured, protect it from the sun and wear a cap for swimming.

AIR TRAVEL
Always dress for comfort particularly on long-haul flights. Wear an easy, comfortable outfit that does not wrinkle. Avoid a tight waistband or binding underwear. Even if it's warm, wear a jacket or sweater over your blouse as it is always cool on a plane. Feet tend to swell during a plane trip so make sure your shoes are not tight. Avoid boots when flying. If you remove them during the trip they will be hard to put on over swollen feet.

Tips when flying
- When the plane begins to take off, yawn frequently. This relaxes your throat muscles and helps prevent your ears popping from the rapid change in pressure. Chewing gum, when the plane takes off and descends, is another good preventive measure.
- Pressurized air dries you out, so it's a good idea to drink a lot of water or juices. Avoid alcohol or caffeine.
- For comfort, you can take your shoes off and wear travel slippers.
- If you like to sleep on a plane, the quietest seats are in front of the engines. For a smooth ride, choose a seat adjacent to the wings. An aisle seat is good if you like to walk around. The best aisle seat on a 747 is in the centre of the plane. For extra-leg room, if you don't mind missing the movie, sit directly underneath the screen.

THE SINGLE WOMAN TRAVELLING ALONE
More women are now travelling alone with the result that hotels, restaurants and airports are becoming better prepared to meet their needs. Many hotels have

parking/garage escorts available and all good hotels will provide you with a bellboy or security person to accompany you if for any reason you feel uncomfortable walking alone to your room at night. It is sensible not to wear too obvious attention-seeking jewellery, if you are staying alone in a hotel.

While women who dine alone are no longer automatically seated by restaurant kitchens, it is sometimes hard to be seated at table when the dining room is crowded. To avoid inconsiderate behaviour, make a reservation beforehand and quietly but firmly insist that your reservation be honoured. If you expect to eat most of your meals at the same hotel or resort dining room it will make a big difference in the way you are treated if, on arrival, you introduce yourself to the Maitre d'; give him a generous tip, tell him how long you'll be staying, and indicate your preference about sitting alone or with a group.

Safety

When walking alone, have some idea of your destination; walk briskly and with confidence. Carry your purse diagonally across your body from shoulder to hip and keep your hand on your purse. In some countries pickpocketing by motor scooter is common.

Don't carry a lot of cash or if you have to, keep it in a money belt worn under your clothing. Check out the unsafe neighbourhoods and don't walk in them.

Don't keep cash, credit cards, travellers cheques in one purse. If the purse is lost or stolen, you will need to have money or credit cards elsewhere.

Bus and train stations are common areas for theft. Keep an eye on your luggage. If alone, try to join a group or a family. If approached by an undesirable stranger, either ignore his advances or look him straight in the eye and tell him to go away.

Airline clubs were once reserved for first class passengers only, but are now available for those who are prepared to pay the reasonable membership fee. These comfortable lounges are pleasant places in which to wait, especially if your flight is delayed.

What is beauty?

IDEAS · OPINIONS · ANSWERS

What do you look for in a woman? Who do you aspire to? What gives a woman that sparkle, style, individuality and flair that makes her stand out from the crowd?

Conversely, when you walk into a room, what image do you project — well-groomed and organised, cool and efficient, soft and feminine? The way you dress should enhance your figure and facial features and make you look interesting enough for people to want to know more about you. What do you have to say that others may share or learn from? It takes effort and discipline to maintain your appearance, look after your health and acquire new interests. But you make the choices and, if you make the right ones, you will be rewarded by looking and feeling great.

> **B**EAUTY IS ALTOGETHER IN THE EYE OF THE BEHOLDER.
>
> Lew Wallace

That subtle quality that we know to be beauty and the essential ingredients required to achieve it are defined by different people in different ways.

Image-makers, people in beauty and those who sell beautiful clothes and jewellery — the fashionable and famous share their ideas with us and help us to reflect upon what we are looking for — that elusive quality that every woman seeks after.

Beauty is . . .

Semiramis Lalvani
(Formerly of Régines)

When I first meet a woman, I don't put emphasis on the details of her clothing, but look for an overall impression of her personality. However, I do admire women who are able to project their personality through their dress. The real beauty of a woman is in her ability to express inner harmony through an exterior image. This is a beauty that goes far beyond a woman's age.

Peter Norman
(Managing Director, Parfums Givenchy)

I notice a woman's attitude, her total presence, her elegance, and the visual impact she makes – until I have the opportunity to discover more.
I find chipped nail varnish and lipstick on teeth very unattractive.
I look for kindness and thoughtfulness in a woman. I like her to be well-groomed even if she's in a pair of jeans.

Lindka Cierach
(Dress designer)

A woman's aura and manner, presence and carriage make the greatest initial impression. Naturally, because of my work, I also notice her clothes and accessories.
I believe a woman's beauty comes from within and that this is achieved through a positive attitude, a balanced lifestyle, exercise, and laughter with a good friend.

Princess Luciana Pignatelli
(Featured in Italian *Vogue*)

It's good to see a nice package – to see somebody who has elegance, somebody who knows how to blend colours and wear clothes. But what I admire most in women is character and quality. What I dislike in women is conceit and malicious gossip.

To look great, I think exercise and diet are the most important things. Make exercise part of your life, like brushing your teeth. My own tip for diet is: fruit for breakfast, vegetables for lunch and oriental food or pasta for dinner. If I had to choose one beauty item, I'd make it mascara because the eyes say it all.

Terry O'Neill
(Photographer)

What I first notice about a woman is her warmth and vulnerability.

The most unattractive thing a woman can do is belittle the man in her life – it's a reflection of her.

The qualities I look for in a woman? We'll start with a beautiful face and lovely legs and figure. The other qualities I look for are warmth, tenderness and a sense of humour.

The two women who I consider great beauties are Michelle Pfeiffer and of course Ava Gardiner.

Roberto Devorik
(Managing Director of Gianni Versace, Jianfranco Serre, Régines)

I admire a woman who carries herself with grace and dignity – one who is feminine and warm.

I dislike a hard, mannish, aggressive woman.

For me, a sexy woman is intelligent and feminine with a sense of style that goes beyond fashion, for example, Jacqueline Bissett or Princess Michael of Kent.

INDEX

Acknowledgements

Special photography   **Tony McGee except pages 23, 68, 75, 133 by Roger Stowell**

Other photography   The publishers would like to thank the following organisations and individuals for their kind permission to reproduce the photographs in this book: Aquascutum 135; Empathy 44 (btm), 46; Susan Griggs Agency/Sandra Lousada 123; Guerlain 17, Robert Harding Picture Library/Alistair Cowin 14; The Image Bank/David Vance 127; Roloff Benny 141 (top); Mark Lawrence 141 (middle); Snowdon 141 (btm); Octopus Group Ltd/Sandra Lousada 40,/Tim Simmons 121; Parfums Givenchy 140 (middle); Alan Olley 140 (btm); Retna Pictures Ltd/Ron Batzdorff 139; Tie Rack 78, 79; Wella Great Britain 44 (top), 47 Tony McGee 51; Portara/W.L. Janda 85.

Styling for Special Photography   **Liz E. London**

Make-up for Special Photography   **Mary-Lou, Ariane, Pat McGraith, Ray Allington**

Hair for Special Photography   **Pascal, Joel O'Sullivan, Ray Allington, Peter Forrester**

Illustrations   **Rosalyn Kennedy, Jan Griffiths**

The publishers would like to thank the following companies for kindly contributing clothes, accessories and other props for the photography: Amanda Charles; Nightingale Lingerie; Mondi; Arabella Pollen; L'Or Noir; Selfridges; Monet; Fendi; Edina Ronay; Bulgari; Harvey Nichols; Shakira Caine; Herbert Johnson; Max Mara; Kenzo; Browns; Alexon; Etienne Aigner; Donna Karen at Browns; Penny Green at Lucienne Phillips; Branchette; Alaïa at Browns; Calvin Klein at Harvey Nichols; Paul Costello; Alison Swift; Sue Pollard; Kellian; Armani; Nicole Farhi; Betty Barclay at Selfridges; Country Casuals; Mulberry; Jaeger at Selfridges; Adrienne Vittadini at Harvey Nichols; Anne Klein; Fenwicks; Trixi Schober at Selfridges; Alexon at Selfridges; Hyde Park Hotel; Byblos; Branché; Marks and Spencer; Marella; Courtenay; Burberry; Kent & Curwen.

Special thanks to   Marian Errickson; Sheila Shiffman and Whittle Communications for research work; Lisa Tai; Anna Mumford; and

ELIZABETH ARDEN

for their generous contribution to the book.

Anna Goodwin   070 . 072   61   546

Anna Goodwin   070 . 072   61   546